Lightness was commissioned by the Netherlands Design Institute

The inevitable
renaissance of minimum
energy structures

**Adriaan Beukers
Ed van Hinte**

010 publishers, Rotterdam 2001

Lightness

Preface

By the year 2040 the world's population will have approximately doubled. People living then will be enjoying an average level of prosperity that is far higher than today. Without changes in production and consumption, that would lead to an unacceptable pressure on the environment. We face the challenge of combining economic growth and greater employment with reducing the impact on the environment, space and nature. Is that possible? Yes, it is. At least, it is if we set our technological sails.

One of the places where work to that end is already going ahead at full speed is the Faculty of Aerospace Engineering at Delft University of Technology. Much research effort there is focused on lightweight structures and fibre-reinforced materials. In a sustainable economy, the guiding principle is 'the lighter the better'. Lighter transport systems and products represent an enormous energy saving. And not only in aerospace applications!

The development of new lightweight materials has led to revolutionary changes in the world around us. Take the tremendous advance of polymers over the past forty years. Their potential applications today are almost numberless: from dairy product packaging to car components, and from carpets to pipelines. Technological developments now enable complete car dashboards to be manufactured from one and the same material. This makes the recycling process far simpler and more energy-efficient.

But research is also capable of improving the application of traditional materials. Take the everyday tin can. Research has shown that a can made with a honeycomb pattern is stronger than a conventional one. Consequently, the can wall may be made thinner without sacrificing any of its strength. The result is that the honeycomb-type can is over 10% lighter than its predecessor. You'll hardly notice any difference when you put that can in your supermarket trolley. But when you think that around 1.4 billion cans are sold every year in the Netherlands, the advantage is obvious.

Space technology often leads to remarkable innovations in other disciplines. Sometimes that can lead to very surprising applications. A well-known example is Marcel Wander's knotted chair. He used aramid fibres from aerospace technology to produce a chair that is entirely made in macramé. The chair's design is so good that the Museum of Modern Art in New York has acquired it.

Materials research, environment, energy conservation, functionality and design: all these aspects are closely interrelated. In this book you will find a fascinating survey of important developments in this field.

dr. G.J. Wijers
Minister of Economic Affairs

008
Introduction

010
A bathtub full of change

022
The trinity essence

032
Tensegrity hero

038
Compression champion

043
Smart by nature

048
Nature as a rolemodel

058
Extra 400

069
Win-win materials

082
Bending for power

088
Fake warfare

094
Reinventing the wheel

102
Trailer gains payload

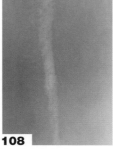

108
Lightweight economics

114
Bridging the gap

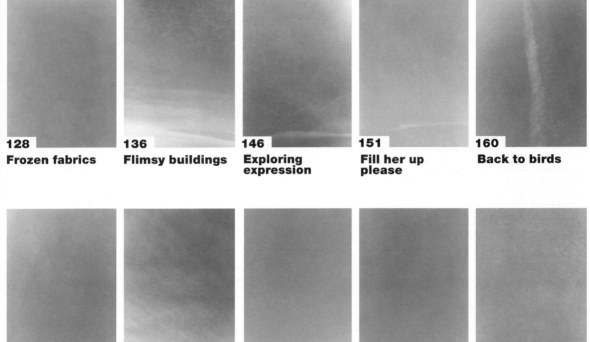

128
Frozen fabrics

136
Flimsy buildings

146
Exploring
expression

151
Fill her up
please

160
Back to birds

164
In depth

179
Glossary

181
Index

183
Bibliography

185
Dutch summary

Intro-
duction

The story of 'Lightness' is not just about airplanes, or composite materials, although they play an important role. It really deals with the building structure of all things made and grown. Reading this book will change the way you look at all objects, even if they are just pictures in the newspaper. It is, essentially, a book on technology, and it will trigger you to look at structures more intensely and see them in a different light. Crossing a bridge or driving a car will be different.

At least, that is what happened to us when we made this book. It was great fun and a stimulating task. It all happened in a rather special way. 'Lightness' is the result of intensive mutual effort between inspiring 'storyteller' Adriaan Beukers, who is one of the managers of the Laboratory for Structures and Materials of the Faculty of Aerospace Engineering at Delft University of Technology, graphic designer Erik Wong and myself. Usually books on these technical subjects are written and designed separately. The writer writes his expert texts and delivers them to the designer, together with a shoe box full of pictures. Next the designer does his organizing, choosing and drafting. We did it together, through many weekly discussions on everything from famous comedy actresses and ballooning accidents all the way to Japanese Zen archers and the silly Dutch habit of exporting pigs to Italy and re-importing them as Parma ham, meanwhile working our way through several thousands of pictures and the stories behind them. During this process we were lovingly and carefully supported by organizer Marjon Beumer from the Netherlands Design Institute. The discussions created an open atmosphere. Somewhere between the lines the book came into being.

It was a complicated job as 'Lightness' deals with many different subjects that, somehow, are all interrelated by analogies, in shape, structure, process, or the idea behind them. Likeness apparently transcends time, origin and professional specialism.

'Lightness' can therefore be read in different ways, depending on one's interest. Its basic sequence is founded on intuitive association rather than a tight and rigid system, except for the beginning. The starting point is that we have to look for novel ways to make things lighter. This is simply inevitable, because otherwise the human race will no longer be able to afford mass transportation of goods and people at increasing speeds.

The quest for efficient structures is firmly rooted in history. When people had to carry their own stuff around lightness was a prerequisite. Ancient and traditional nomadic cultures have made and are still making artifacts in ways that may be instructive to designers, architects and engineers alike. Nature provides many examples as well, as natural forces and processes always lead to minimum energy structures on different scale levels. The smallest living organism cannot survive without minimizing inner structural stress under all circumstances, and earthquakes are our home planet's Prozac.

The book's most important angle is the trinity of material, shape and process, since the balance between them becomes more delicate, proportional to the lightness required for the resulting structure. Making things lighter is not just a matter of choosing lighter materials, for every material entails its own properties in terms of shape and manufacturing techniques. Moreover, a complex structure consists of a hierarchy of elements. Focusing attention on making just one minor element lighter than it was before, may result in a weight increase for the entire construction. This is caused by the necessity to compensate for weaknesses that are the result of imbalanced weight reduction.

From here onwards the book is meant to be an entertaining mixture of the explanation of the promise of new composite materials, and inspiring examples that give the reader insight into the way structures work. We can learn just as much from Antoni Gaudí's mistakes as we can from Otto Liliënthal's successes. Desert tents can contribute to our knowledge just as well as giraffes or stealth bombers. Experts can find additional information at the back of the book.

Some of the described examples, such as the 'Extra 400' airplane, the 'Cold Feather' trailer, the flexible containers and the Dry-Tech project are part of the work at the Laboratory. Nevertheless the purpose of this book is not so much to describe these objects. They do, however, have certain instructive capacities that add to our understanding of lightness.

'Lightness' is the 1997 Theo Limperg Award. It was given to the Faculty of Aerospace Engineering of the University of Technology in Delft.

The judges in particular stressed the personal role of Adriaan Beukers (who himself put a lot of work into this book). The judges' decision was informed principally by the stimulating and pioneering role played by the faculty in the field of industrial design engineering. In particular, research conducted into new fibre-reinforced materials and structures has been of crucial significance.

Ed van Hinte

A bathtub full of change

Left: The automobile is slowly
reaching the end of its potential.

The rich Chinese businessman leaves his hotel in
Montreal and gets into his 72 kilogram Russian chauf-
feur driven 2148 kilogram Mercedes 300 SE whilst carrying his French ultra light carbon fibre reinforced
plastic briefcase. Unknowingly he demonstrates that
we can observe strange paradoxical clashes between
the formerly accepted idea that there is no end to
earth resources, and the seeds of insight that lightness
may help improve the quality of life. Slowly but
inevitably we are becoming aware of the fact that the
price we pay for energy is unjustifiably low and part of
the slash and burn culture that has become too familiar to be noticed. In the near future lightness will, however, once again turn into an accepted starting point
for the way we construct things.

There is a new law in the Netherlands that aims to protect workers from carrying burdens heavier than 25

kilograms, for instance when loading trucks. It shows the vast discrepancy between the power of transport equipment, that can easily carry tons over endless distances, and human strength. Up until a few centuries ago, people themselves were the measure by which maximum load was determined. Nowadays the power of cranes, ships, trucks and airplanes defines the standard. The thing is, that none of these manpower saving heavy tools can do without the input of enormous amounts of energy.

All constructions are related to transport in one way or another. They are load for at least a part of their lives and in many cases they are vehicles themselves. The evolution and the change in relative importance of construction materials over history is remarkable. The graph in the shape of a not very comfortable bathtub, as drawn by Ashby, roughly shows what happened in the past and what is bound to happen in the future. Some ten thousand years ago most people led nomadic lives. They wandered around to hunt or to gather food, minerals, materials for shelter and whatever else they needed to survive. To be able to travel around they had to rely on light simple tools, most of which were made out of materials they could find anywhere: natural polymer based wood, bone, skin, horn and hair, and simple composites such as mixtures of straw and mud. Stone, bone and flint and clay were used to make weapons and pottery. Metals were hardly available in the early times.

Gradually nomadism turned into settling and urbanization. The decreasing need for carrying around all their possessions made people realize they could use more durable materials and housing. They started to make buildings out of wattle-and-daub. stone and wooden beams, and discovered the melting power of fire and consequently the possibilities of copper, bronze and

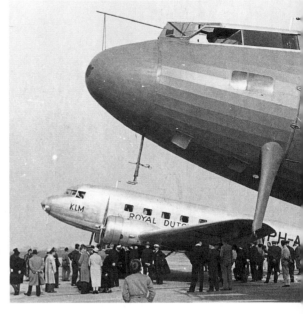

PROSPERITY AND SUFFOCATION

Sooner or later improvement comes to an end. Generally speaking technological development can be represented by what is known as the 'S-curve'. The vertical direction of this lifecycle graph shows increase in performance in any type of property: the maximum age of a dinosaur, the effectiveness of antibiotics, the maximum height for polevaulting, the strength of riveted joints. On the horizontal line there is effort. In the beginning it takes a lot of time and money to achieve relatively small improvements. After a while, however, every successful property tends to prosper and improve quickly. Then, after a period of steady innovative progress the rate of improvement diminishes and finally suffocates at the top of the curve, because competition is taking over. The wise thing to do before suffocation is to start something new, jump to the beginning of a different concept with a fresh S-curve. The broad metal area in

'There have been magnificent and refined inventions and evolutions in the past. We can learn a great deal from the concepts that already exist.'

Ashby's graph on the next page tells us that there have been enormous amounts of conceptual jumps within the development of metal structures in a relatively short period of time. The now occuring widening of the polymer and composite zone shows that starting S-curves with these materials is very promising indeed.

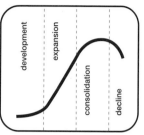

development | expansion | consolidation | decline

A true S-curve drama. In 1934 KLM decided to buy the Douglas DC-2 based on an aluminium stressed skin construction instead of the Fokker F-36 that still consisted of steel wires and tubes, linen and wood.

Inauguration of the Fokker F-32 in Los Angeles 1932.

iron. Metals proved their extreme versatility particularly during the past two millennia.

Unprecedented in history is the development in new applications and the discovery of many new materials over the last 150 years: steel, aluminium, titanium, and synthetic polymers, artificial ceramics, to name a few. Even for metals limits cannot be stretched endlessly. Ashby's curve shows that, in comparison with other materials, they reached their maximum contribution to constructions in and around World War Two. From then on synthetic ceramics, polymers and composites began competing and will continue to do so for many years to come. The reason that application of metals is gradually decreasing is not that metal resources are being exhausted, but that the most widely used ones, steel and aluminium, are no longer capable of meeting long term requirements of price and performance. Research and development to achieve small improve-

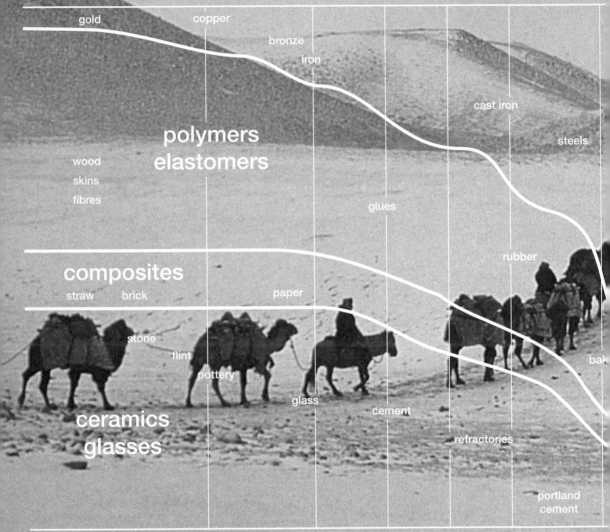

relative importance

gold   copper

                        bronze

                        iron

                                                cast iron

                                                steels

polymers
elastomers

wood

skins

fibres

                                        glues

composites

straw   brick   paper

                                                rubber

stone

flint

pottery   bak

glass

ceramics   cement
glasses

                                        refractories

                                                portland
                                                cement

10.000 BC   5.000 BC   0   1000   1500   1800   190

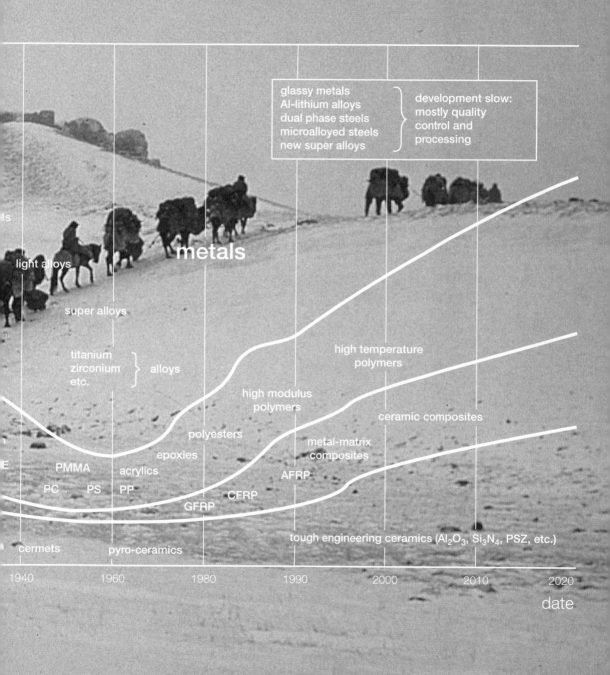

glassy metals
Al-lithium alloys
dual phase steels
microalloyed steels
new super alloys
} development slow: mostly quality control and processing

ls

light alloys

metals

super alloys

titanium
zirconium } alloys
etc.

high temperature
polymers

high modulus
polymers

ceramic composites

polyesters

metal-matrix
composites

E   PMMA   acrylics   epoxies

PC   PS   PP   AFRP

GFRP   CFRP

cermets   pyro-ceramics   tough engineering ceramics (Al$_2$O$_3$, Si$_3$N$_4$, PSZ, etc.)

1940   1960   1980   1990   2000   2010   2020

date

ments are becoming relatively expensive.
Interestingly the evolution in engineering polymers and composites, as observed by Ashby, coincides with change in the importance of weight. Whereas in prehistoric times man had to be able to carry things himself, heaviness became less important as he got more help from animals, slaves and, later on, from engines. Now lightness, or performance per energy unit, is quickly gaining significance again because of the aforementioned reason: cheap energy is getting scarce.
A major factor that plays into the game of polymers and composites is their low density. As the price of fossil fuels is expected to rise and human civilization is getting more and more dependent on transport of goods and people, with continually increasing speeds, lightness of structures becomes crucial to technological and economical development.
Transport of goods and people is characterized by rather peculiar constant factors, throughout history as well as across cultures. Take for instance the ancient way of long-distance transport by caravan across the

The railway and subway network in Tokyo is so extensive that it never takes more than ten minutes from the front door to a train.

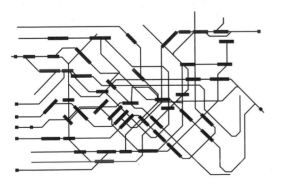

deserts of Asia and Africa. In the early days, at least four thousand years ago, food for pack animals was readily available and free. Therefore trade transport was not expensive. Later on people settled along the trails and caravans had to travel through areas that became gradually more densely populated. Drovers had to pay large sums of money for grazing their mules and camels. Moreover they risked being attacked by bandits.
The Islamic justice system found a remarkable solution for this problem of costs in founding subsidized 'caravanserais'. They were the predecessors of modern motels, except that they were free of charge.
Caravans, usually consisting of one or two drovers and some twelve animals, were allowed to stay in for three days to recover, and to stock food and cattle cake for the next stage.
This accommodation kept down the costs of transport on the major trade routes and thereby allowed caravan drovers to compete with seafarers who had free wind energy at their disposal.
The costs were extremely low. Not much quantitative information is available, but we do know that towards

'The high frequency of Japanese public transportation covers up delays.'

'The personal transportation budget amounts to three percent of the net income throughout the world.'

the end of the sixteenth century, an as-the-crow-flies 2200 kilometre caravan transport of silk didn't amount to more than about three percent of the selling price. This happens to be a kind of universal tacit standard, as today transport costs of most articles are usually related to the total price in exactly the same way. The implication is clear: building caravanserais to cheapen transport no longer makes any sense, but we can get the same effect by saving on the cost of transport per unit weight. Transport needs less energy if we both develop lighter vehicles and reduce the weight of transported goods and packaging.

The weight of an average human being, however, is not something that can easily be changed by advanced engineering. We do know that people themselves often are the payload of transport equipment. As a matter of fact each and every person travels an average of between an hour and an hour and a half every day. An interesting survey by Schafer and Victor, recently pub-

THE WEIGHT RACE

The quality of cars tends to be associated with their weight and safety in traffic, in a rather egotistic way that is. A heavy car may be safe to its passengers, but to all and everything outside it, the moving ton of steel is a lethal projectile that one needs to protect oneself against by using an even safer and heavier vehicle. Despite the fact that the share of polymers in car constructions is gradually increasing, automobiles keep on getting heavier. The result is that the world is burdened by huge amounts of material moving around without

serving any other purpose than providing an illusion of safety and comfort. A small study shows that the car price per kilogram increases proportional to weight. Although extremely weighty models such as the Rolls Royce seem to be superseded, Daimler Benz is still accommodating the rich driver with newly developed expensive heavy toys. In fact the company has overdone it with its new S-class. The limit for passenger cars in Germany is 2410 kilograms which implies that the driver will need a truck license if he wants to carry three passengers. Data from the American board for traffic safety (NHTSA) show that from 1985 until 1992 car companies paid over $233 million in environmental

car price (CP) / price per kilo (PPK)

DM/kilo

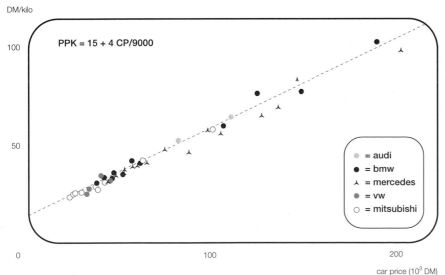

$$PPK = 15 + 4\ CP/9000$$

- ● = audi
- ● = bmw
- ⅄ = mercedes
- ● = vw
- ○ = mitsubishi

car price (10^3 DM)

Left: The heavier the car the more expensive it becomes per unit weight. (source Willem van Dreumel)

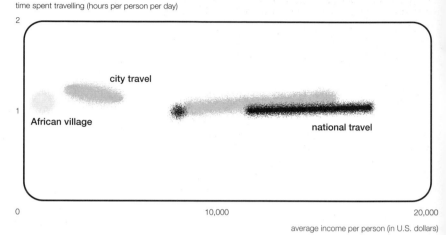

time spent travelling (hours per person per day)

fines. The share of BMW and Mercedes together amounted to little over $150 million. The companies claim that they prefer paying the fines because otherwise they would have to diminish the weight of their products and they couldn't guarantee their safety any longer. It's about time we had a car weight armistice.

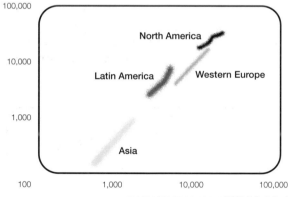

per capita traffic volume (passenger-kilometres)

lished in Scientific American, suggests that this 'travel-time budget' is the same all over the world. It holds true for African villagers as well as for the aforementioned Mercedes owning businessman, who by the way happens to live in Seattle. The differences are in covered distance and, because of that, in speed. People with a higher income will simply travel faster and further.

FLYING OCEAN STEAMERS

One famous S-curve is buried in Lakehurst, New Jersey. That is the place where the airliner Hindenburg burned in the year 1937. It was the last of a dynasty of 119 rigid airships or zeppelins. They had a complicated hand made aluminium internal framework that enclosed several balloons. Building something as huge and complicated as that is no longer affordable. The balloons were secured in place by a netting that transmitted the lifting force of their gas to the structure. Each balloon had valves, which operated automatically to relieve pressure when the gas expanded with altitude. The pilot could release gas too. A complicated ballast system with water served to do the opposite. When part of it was released, the airship ascended to a cruising altitude where the engines supplied propulsion. As fuel was consumed, the airship became lighter and tended to climb. Too much height resulted in a release of gas into the

'For most members of the European parliament the ratio between travel time and work time is out of balance.'

atmosphere. In the case of helium this was a costly way of controlling the ship.

The first successful non rigid airship, or blimp as it is called today, was built in 1852 by Henri Giffard. It was powered by a steam engine. This type is still in use on a limited scale, in a battery powered electric version. It has no internal structure but a skin made of textile impregnated with rubber for gas tightness. Inside the gas space of the hull are two or more air diaphragms called ballonets that are kept under slight pressure. These exert pressure upon the gas that stiffens the shape and creates a smooth flying surface. On takeoff the ballonets are almost fully inflated, but as the airship gains altitude and the gas expands, air is let out. In World War II, the United States used airships. The navy used them for minesweeping

and antisubmarine patrols. Blimps are not fast, but whereas an airplane can remain airborne for only a few hours, an airship could stay aloft for 60 hours. The most long-lasting use of airships has been by the Goodyear Tire and Rubber Company. Their first, the Pony was built in 1919. The newest, the Spirit of Akron, which

Graphs: Top left: The time spent travelling per day is the same all over the world. Left: The higher the income the further people travel in the same amount of time. Below: People with a higher income travel with faster means of transportation. It is remarkable that the relative share of cars is already decreasing in the US.

On the basis of a constant travel-time budget and increasing incomes, the authors have made a projection of future developments in world traffic. They think that by 2050 automobiles will provide only about 35 percent (53 percent in 1990) of the total traffic volume, whereas high speed transport with airplanes and fast trains will account for over 40 percent. This doesn't imply that cars will disappear. High speed travelling will only account for a fraction of the total travel time of an hour and a half. In the view of Schafer and Victor the contribution of low-speed public transportation to traffic volume will decrease to a little under 25 percent. The theory that people will travel faster in the future is not improbable. Combined with the fact that sustainability of energy resources and the world's resilience against pollution are limited, the main conclusion is, again, that we have to learn to travel light.

Now let us return to Ashby's graph. As we have seen, it illustrates that light constructions are now reappearing

share of traffic volume (percent of passenger-kilometres)

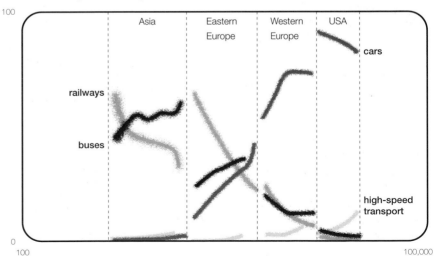

average income per person (in 1985 U.S. dollars)

'The fact that politicians of all convictions throughout the hierarchy are interested in Zeppelins should arouse suspicion.'

Above: Lightweight composite city bus weighing 999 kilograms.

Left: The bridge of the Hindenburg flying at approximately 111 knots.

was launched in 1989, was for a short time the world's largest operating airship. It was surpassed in size in 1991 by the 68 metres long Sentinel 1000, built by Westinghouse Airships, who have recently developed the Sentinel 5000, twice the length of its predecessor, but still smaller than the largest rigid ship ever built. The craft will be refillable in the air, with the help of helicopters based on the ship. That is essentially what they were: ships. Over the past few years the attention for airships has been growing. They are supposed to be an environmentally friendly transport alternative. It is questionable whether they will succeed, regarding the trend of increasing need for speed. If people want to travel for the sake of travelling itself from A to B, C, F, L and V and then back to A, like they do on a cruise ship, an airship may be an entertaining alternative to Love Boat. However, it is not fast enough by far to fulfil a significant roll in a world where the time between departure and arrival is expected to be negligible.

in the history of human culture albeit for different reasons. What are usually presented as new and modern technological developments – tent-like architecture, polymers with or without reinforcement, composites, and their applications – existed thousands of years. Some ancient technologies are still around in other than western cultures.

Therefore developing light structures is by no means jumping in at the deep end. We can learn quite a lot about the use of so called high-tech materials and ways to make and work and apply them by studying objects and technologies from early times, that were created by ancient craftsmen with shaman-like mystic insight. Just like them we can observe light and strong structures that nature produces and try to mimic them. New developments usually thrive on everything we already happen to know. <

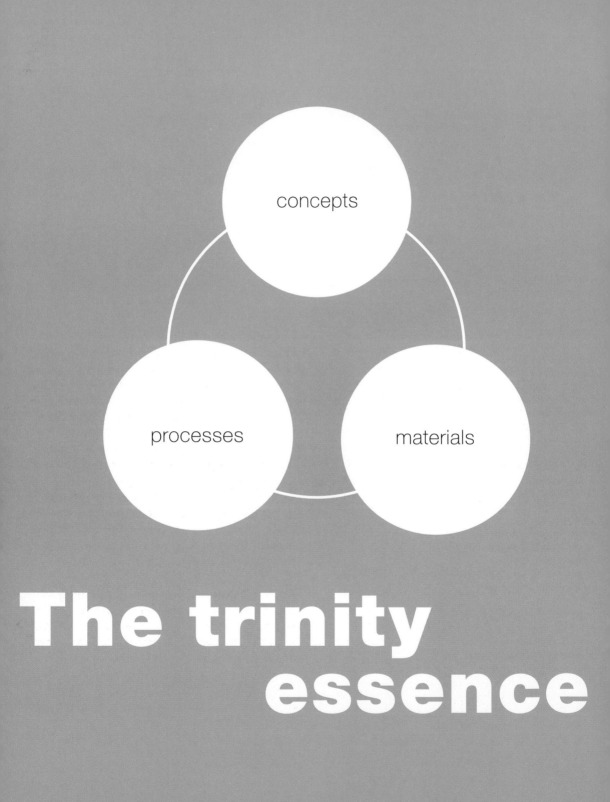

The trinity
essence

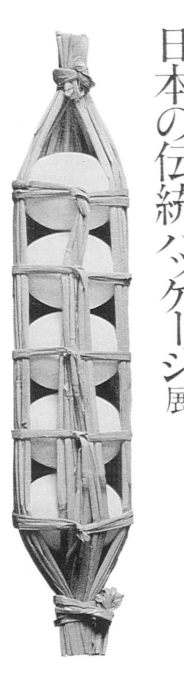

うつの卵はいかにして包まれたか

日本の伝統。パッケージ展

Eggs can be packed by simply and carefully tying them together with rice leaves. The eggs themselves are part of the concept.

Stacked beer bottles, a hole in the ground, piled up stones, wattle-and-daub, wooden beams, cloth, ice, animal skins, bamboo, welded steel bars: shelter can be made out of anything in any way and in many different shapes, as long as weight doesn't really matter. Every single functional object that we make evolves from a process that turns material into a functional shape, the inevitable trinity of technology. There is no shape without material and effort.

The more we value lightness and minimum energy consumption, the more critical this eternal trinity becomes. There are no kites made out of concrete, because up until now nobody has come up with a process that can provide concrete with a shape that can be flown on a piece of string.

Still, the implication of the technological trinity is not that light objects should by definition be made out of the lightest possible material. There are indeed concrete sailing ships and although aluminium may have proved a suitable material for constructing airplanes, it is not the material with the lowest density. What matters is that it is a light metal that can be shaped to perform as an airplane.

As a matter of fact the first glider airplanes hardly contained any metal. Like prehistoric structures they were chiefly made out of wood and textiles: lighter than any metal, and made into different shapes according to different production processes that were available at that time, when aluminium was still an extremely expensive gleaming curiosity. Given the fact that early airplane materials are extremely light and that we seem to have reached the end of improvement in metal constructions – don't forget Ashby's bathtub – , there is a marked indication that striving for lightness strongly needs development of knowledge on building things out of lighter materials. These happen to be the organic ones: polymers and composites. They are light simply because their main building stones are the lighter atoms: hydrogen, nitrogen, oxygen and carbon and they can be composed into materials of great strength. Apart from the choice of materials, constructions have to be efficient in order to be light. Building efficient constructions puts the issue of constructing economically in a different perspective. For economic reasons most objects contain many standard semimanufactures, such as sheet, bars and beams, that have been

Computer simulation shows that cans build up natural resistance against buckling by generating hexagonal deformation patterns.

Otto Liliënthal derived his ideas for airplane construction and materials directly from the examples nature provides.

CANS CAN BE LIGHT

Heavy materials may be shaped into light objects. Constructing for lightness is a delicate matter of harmony between material, shape and production process. Tin plate is quite heavy if you try to lift a roll of it. Still it can be made into relatively light food containers, and even lighter ones if you consider the recent improvement in can design.

It originated from a coincidence in the laboratory of German physicist Frank Mirtsch towards the end of the seventies. He discovered that a tin cylinder under pressure with steel rings on the inside, deformed in regular square patterns at unreinforced places, thus strengthening it. This led to the assumption that a honeycomb pattern might result in even greater strength and stiffness, and that thinner tin plate would be needed to produce cans. Every hundredth of a millimetre counts in the vast numbers that cans are produced in.

Further research finally resulted in the 'Hexacan'. The main difficulty that had to be overcome was not so much the shape, but the labelling. It can't be done with paper, but the manufacturer has found a way of dealing with this problem by applying printed plastic. The honeycomb can weighs 10 to 15 percent less than its conventional predecessor. And that is quite a lot, considering the billions of containers produced every year, 1.4 billion in the Netherlands alone. Hexacan will be on your shelves soon if it is not there already.

'We must realize that natural materials are in fact structures.'

'Weight saving is obstructed by the fact that in design most thumb rules are expressed in terms of material cost per unit weight.'

In comparison with the cold, heavy and generally uncomfortable ring mail glove the knitted aramid version for professional butchers is a perfect fulfilment of the trinity of concept, material and process.

length. It is the length expressed in kilometres that a thread of material can hang down without breaking through mere gravity. According to the same principle the maximum span of bridges can be calculated for different materials for every construction principle. Efficiency of course also involves making materials do what they do best. Wood is not very good at taking pressure. Concrete is. Steel, and fibres made from glass, aramid, polyethene and carbon all are extremely good at withstanding tension. Horn, bone and ceramics can deal with compression.

The wise thing to do, if you want to build something light, therefore is to take care that the construction leads to a clear differentiation between pure tension and pure compression, and that the materials are chosen according to their best abilities to deal with these forces. A fine example is the small composite bow that was used by the nomadic tribes of the Eurasian plains in ancient times. In fact it was so small they could shoot it on horseback while riding. It consisted of several layers of different materials glued together. Its core consisted of wood. The front end had to be able to deal with tension and was made out of sinew. The back,

worked to fit specific applications. As these materials possess standard qualities and measures, they are generally oversized in some places. An aluminium airplane would be lighter if, for instance, skin thickness were not dictated by availability on the market, but by strength and stiffness.

The most obvious implication of composing efficiently is, that constructions shouldn't suffer under the burden of their own weight. Materials should be able to transfer as much energy as possible relative to their density. There are several ways to express this property. For example there is a theoretical value called break

This unusual design for the periodic system of elements by Niels Bohr clearly puts the lighter elements at the top of a hierarchy.

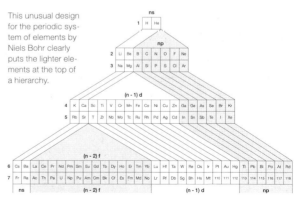

Below left: Ancient building structures clearly demonstrate the primitive supremacy of compression and bending forces.

DEALING WITH FORCE

'Every beam must deflect under the load which is applied to it and will therefore be distorted into a curved or bent shape. Material on the concave or compression face of a bent beam will be shortened or strained in compression. Material on the convex or tension face will be lengthened or strained in tension.'
This phenomenon, described by J.E. Gordon in his book 'Structures, or why things don't fall down' is all too common. The convex side of a bent metal tube is stretched, while the material on the inside of the bend is butted. A bend in a square metal profile with the characteristic deformations even has its own name: the 'American bend'.
If you break a wooden slat by bending it, you will notice that the material on the concave face is the part that yields. That is because the wood structure is not very good at resisting compression forces. Bending a brick is not quite as easy, but in the end the force will cause it to come apart on the opposite side. Brick, like most ceramic materials is not very strong under tension. As materials usually are strong either under tension or under compression and bending causes both kinds of stress, it is not a very efficient way of dealing with force. It is wiser to make a choice and apply a material best suited to either of the two.

Exploitation of tension stress leads to slender and light constructions.

however, had to be strong enough to deal with the considerable compression forces that occurred, not just during shooting, but also while the bow was just bent. It was made out of horn.
Of course withstanding either pure tension or pure compression is not just a question of material, but also of construction. The best one-dimensional way of tension transfer is through short fibres twined or wrought together in threads, ropes and cables. The bowstring represents this kind of construction, and so does the ancient wire bridge across the yawning abyss that heroes and villains alike always cut through in movies. Even the most modern bridges can support traffic because the carrying structure hangs on cables that are usually made out of steel.
As tension generally can be guided through thin threads of light materials, the emphasis in light constructions is on tension even though in constructions that are closed within themselves all tension has to be compensated with compression one way or another.

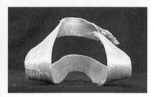

The perfect solution for steel – in this case the shape is optimized to withstand bending – cannot simply be made lighter by replacing the metal with composite. Truly thinking in composites generates a totally different object.

The inside construction of Buckminster Fuller's Dymaxion House and Caproni's non flying failure are perfect examples of wrong materials in wrong concepts made in the wrong way. In Fuller's case: it is not very wise to try and bend corrugated aluminium.

Gordon compares hanging a certain load from a steel rod (tension) and supporting it with a steel tube (compression). In his example the tube has to be no less than 50 times heavier.

The American architect Buckminster Fuller was a great advocate of light constructions and he even invented his own vocabulary, involving words like 'tensegrity' and 'dymaxion', to describe what he saw as ideal construction principles.

The membrane can be considered as the two-dimensional upgrade of the simplest of all rope constructions. It can be made out of different materials depending on its function. Goat skin for instance, can be worked in such a way that it is air tight, to serve as an inflatable swimming aid. The Assyrians used it and it probably is the ancient predecessor of the life belt. Watertightness is another option. In desert countries skin is used to transport beverages and other fluids. And in the west the development of the membrane as a fluid container is continuing. In some countries milk is contained in plastic bags. New textile reinforced flexibles will be used to produce small beer bags that are due to appear on the market soon.

Another well known application of two-dimensional tension resistant fabric is the tent structure. Textiles of different kinds are stretched with cables on supporting structures that take care of the compression forces. Tents have existed for a long time. They are light enough to function as transportable shelters.

HOW TO BUILD A TREE

Wood is unlike any other material in that it really is a complicated construction. Starting out from the micro level wood consists of specially hardened crystalline cells filled with an amorphous substance. The wall of the wood cell consists of cellulose and lignin. Cellulose constitutes 70 percent of the dry cell wall. Lignin fills the spaces within the cellulose network. Cellulose consists of long chains of glucose molecules polymerized into carbohydrate. It is arranged in long, threadlike fibrils. Cellulose wound in this fashion is as strong as an

'It is the fate of new materials that they are always more expensive than the ones they have to replace. The only way for them to be convincing is through cheap constructions and processes.'

equivalent thickness of steel. Lignins also add rigidity to the cell wall. Materials like plastic or metal foams possess the same characteristics. But there is more to a tree than cellulose fibrils, as Gordon shows: 'The first thing that a modern engineer does with a tree is to cut it up into small pieces, which he then glues together again - preferably into some kind of hollow section. It is only recently that we have realized that, after all, the tree does know a thing or two. Among other subtleties, the wood in various parts of the trunk grows in such a way that it is prestressed.' The mechanism behind this is not entirely clear. One assumption is that the trunk loses moisture through its bark. This results in a decrease of volume, which causes tensile stress in the outer wood and compression in the core. It is exactly the

opposite of the prestress man creates in concrete. In the case of a tree trunk the implication is better resistance to bending, because compressive stress at the concave side is, to a certain extent, compensated for by the 'built-in' tensile stress. In fact the effective bending strength is roughly doubled. So cutting and gluing is not always the smart thing to do.

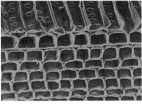

Top: the micro level: cellulose acetate. Middle: cross section of a tree. Above: cell structure.

Kublai Khan was even meaner and more romantic than his grandfather Genghis.

Genghis Khan even had a tent put up on a platform on wheels and because of this may be considered the inventor of the stretched limo.

More and more architects think tent. There are quite a few examples of new buildings that involve tent like roof constructions. They don't necessarily have to be made out of textile materials, however. A beautiful example of a pseudo-membrane, made out of a metal cable structure filled up with transparent polycarbonate tiles, is the roof of the Olympic Stadium in Munich, designed by architect Frei Otto, who has been an advocate of tented structures all his life.

Pure compression in one dimension can best be dealt with by a column, or a wall for that matter, which is in fact nothing but a lot of columns next to each other. It gets more complicated if there is to be a hole in the wall to pass through or to allow a river to stream on. The most efficient way to solve this problem is to build an arch. Gordon: 'The structural function of an arch is to support the downward loads which come upon it by

Minimum use of material can provide optimum functionality. It can do so in different ways with different materials. Steel, stone, textile, concrete, aluminium and composite materials all come with their specific structures depending on the kind of stress they have to deal with. Tension stress is always preferable, since compression and bending require thickness.

turning them into a lateral thrust which runs round the ring of the arch and pushes the voussoirs (arch stones) against each other'. The true master of building stone arches was the Catalan architect Antonio Gaudi, whose Sagrada Familia in Barcelona is still being built. And again: the material to build arches does not have to be stone. Bamboo and different species of grass are very well suited to building arches, simply by bending them. Depending on the required properties of shelter, bunches of bent reed can be frozen into their newly acquired shape by impregnating them with mud. This is in principle the same treatment that glass, or aramide or carbon fibres get when they need to be fixed in a certain shape, the difference being that instead of mud we use synthetic plastics. <

See 'in depth' for more information.

Tensegrity hero

Including a swimming pool, a gymnasium and a library, elevators and even furniture, the twelve storey apartment tower was to weigh about 45 tons. Architect and inventor Richard Buckminster Fuller (1895-1983) designed it in the Twenties to be mass produced and transferred to its destination by Zeppelin.

Fuller was not your average architect. Throughout his life he was a true visionary. More than any of his contemporary colleagues – Oud, Le Corbusier, you name them – he was obsessed with applying the principles of advanced mass industry, especially in the realm of ships and airplanes, to buildings and transportation. He was mainly concerned with construction efficiency and its mathematics. Moreover he always considered the entire context of his designs. He even developed the idea of recycling buildings.

As a youngster he learned to appreciate the technology of ship construction and fishery with its different kinds of tension systems applied in nets. He experienced the idiosyncrasies of yarns and textiles used for sails and learned to mend nets. In his own words the applied tension techniques were 'as original as the ones used by spiders'. Around 1925 he decided to devote himself entirely to research in art and science and to delve into future fulfilment of primary human needs.

At that time the building and car industries were lagging behind in constructive quality. Half a million homes were built and five million autos. He didn't like the fact that the car industry was not interested in applying the principle of maximum performance per kilogram material, which was crucial in the development of Fuller's ideas.

In 1927 he designed the described building. It didn't consist of stacked up bricks and no concrete was involved. Instead the hexagonal floors were hung from a central pylon made out of aluminum pipes, that con-

The two main principles employed by Buckminster Fuller were tensegrity (continuous tension compensated with discontinuous compression) resulting in the design of geodesic domes and Dymaxion (maximum benefit with minimum energy). The car below is a famous example.

The concept of prefabricated building structures is omnipresent and not very new at all.

tained all the main conveniences: elevators, drainage, electrical power, climate regulation, etcetera. All compression and tension loads were absorbed by a stiff triangular framework and cables, anchored in the ground, held the building upright.

Two years later Fuller designed a one family home with five to six rooms that involved the same construction principles and became known as the 'Dymaxion House'. Its height was 12 metres and its diameter 15 metres. Still it didn't weigh more than 2720 kilograms, including furniture and conveniences. Dymaxion is a combination of dynamics, maximum and ion. The notion stands for creating maximum benefit with minimum use of energy and materials under complete application of all scientific and technological means. It has a mathematical meaning too: vector balance. All his construction systems were derived from the tetrahedron as the basic element, which in its turn was derived from the closest packing of spheres. Dymaxion is reached with twelve spheres surrounding one, all touching each other.

In 1933 Buckminster Fuller developed the idea for Dymaxion transport, culminating in the innovative Dymaxion Car, a three wheeled vehicle (two in the front, one at the back) for 11 passengers, that could do 150 kilometres per hour consuming 6.25 litres of fuel every hundred kilometres, which wasn't much in those days and still isn't.

After the development of another self containing Wichita House he developed an interest in synergetic building systems. They are characterized by the whole performing better than the sum of its elements. The forces in a construction system generate tension and compression stresses. Fuller observed that throughout history mankind had been inclined to exploit the compression resistance of available materials, by piling up

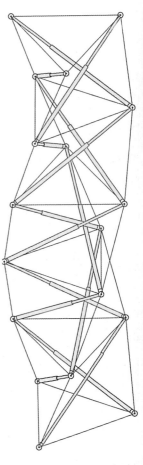

One continuous cable guides all the tension forces, counteracted by the short thick compression elements. Every extension of a tensegrity structure makes it more efficient.

heavy stones for instance. The disadvantage of compression in slender constructions is the phenomenon of buckling. It occurs when bars, shells or plates are thin perpendicular to the direction of the load. Exploitation of tension on the other hand, seems to lead to virtually limitless strength no matter what cross section is chosen. That is why the combination of interrupted compression in relatively short bars and continuous tension in long bars and cables, which Fuller applied intuitively in his first designs, proved successful. Continuous tension or 'tensegrity' helped construct the geodesic domes based on triangular frames. In refined tensegrity constructions parts under compression are separated from those under tension, which is continuously transmitted across all structural components. Interestingly as a result of this these synergetic constructions become relatively lighter and therefore more efficient as they grow, so there is no limit to size. And they can be small as well. A particular sphere shaped carbon molecule (C60) that was discovered some years ago was named after Fuller: 'bucky balls' or 'fullerenes'. <

Building a geodesic dome is
a repeating of modular elements.

'The weakness of a single tensegrity structure is that it is vulnerable. If one element breaks the whole thing falls apart.'

To be able to contribute to the 'Sagrada Familia' cathedral in Barcelona, masons have to be extremely skilful. The building – still not finished, although it was started in the Twenties – consists of classic materials, but its construction principles are unprecedented. Nothing is straight. The immense church looks like it is growing out of the earth like a plant.

Its architect Antoni Gaudi i Cornet (1852-1926) was not a man of theory. Once he told a visitor to his work-shop: 'You want to know what I use for an example? A real tree. It carries its branches, that carry twigs,

Compression champion

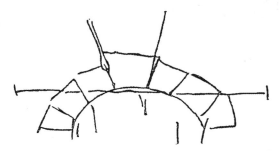

Stone arch for a porch suggested by Heinrich von Kleist in his letter to Wilhelmina von Zenge. It shows that gravity actually prevents an arch from collapsing by turning all forces into compression stress.

which carry the leaves. And each part grows harmonically because the artist God created it.'

Gaudí was inspired by nature, but not in the same way his Jugendstil contemporaries were, for they merely applied organic ornaments to buildings that were otherwise traditional. The master of compression as we have learnt to appreciate him, looked at the characteristics of trees and plants in less superficial ways. Beside his application of exuberant and colourful ornamentation to express himself as an artist, he wanted to learn from nature's constructions and to try and mimic their way of defying gravity.

He disliked the artificial support system of gothic arches that were en vogue among the neo-gothic architects of his time, and disparagingly calling them 'crutches'. He felt he could in some way complete the old style without the extra supporting structures of arches and pillars. Strange crooked columns were his entirely new solution. The clearest example of them can be found in the crypt he built for a worker's colony 'Colònia Güell', in the outskirts of Barcelona.

Organic treelike structures soon became Gaudí's trademark. He had a straightforward method of determining the slantedness of his columns. There were no calculations involved. They would have been impossible anyway as the complex analysis by division of continuous mechanics into smaller parts by means of the 'finite elements method' had yet to be invented. Eiffel, the designer of the tower, gets the credits for first

CLAUDIA SCHIFFER'S WEAKNESS

Slender bodies have their own particular way of failing under compression. Even weight lifters need a belt to prevent them from cracking in the middle. This phenomenon is called structural instability, or rather buckling. It can best be described as a sudden sideward movement in thin material under compressive stress. J.E. Gordon in his book 'Structures' provides us with the most obvious example: 'Take a piece of paper and compress it lengthwise.' Beside the risk of structural failure, buckling does have positive protective effects: where would grass be if it couldn't buckle elastically under our feet? The German-Swiss mathematician Euler in the 18th century was the first one to analyse buckling. He came up with this formula for the buckling load of a strut. (below left) In this surprisingly simple expression P represents the load, E is Young's Modulus, a measurable

various Euler conditions

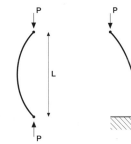

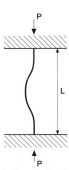

both ends pin-jointed

$$P = \pi^2 \frac{E \cdot I}{L^2}$$

P = maximum load
E = Young's modulus

one end *encastré*, the other pin-jointed and free to move sideways

$$P = \pi^2 \frac{E \cdot I}{4 L^2}$$

both ends fixed in direction and position

$$P = 4 \pi^2 \frac{E \cdot I}{L^2}$$

coming up with the idea of this method, which nowadays predicts deformation and stresses on thousands of computer screens.

Instead the architect determined the proportions and the shape of his buildings with the help of hand-made models, not the usual kind, but compositions of pieces of string and balance weights that he hung upside down. By these simple funicular models he was able to let gravity do the difficult work: determine the bends. The strings hung down in loops in a masterful composition of catenaries. All Gaudí had to do, in a manner of speaking, was have masons copy the structure in stone with the loops pointing upwards. We know he made the basic structural design for his cathedral in this way and he may have applied the same method for determining the proportions of a 300 metre high skyscraper hotel in New York that was never built but would no doubt have relegated the Chrysler Building to second place as an icon.

Gaudí's basic idea was quite ingenious. He reasoned that, if gravity pulled the construction in its right shape, this very composition would be able to withstand gravity if built with the catenaries pointing upwards, turning the load from pure tension to pure compression. Unfortunately reality is not all that simple. So far none of his masterful buildings have collapsed and most of them probably never will. They are stable under their own weight. However, some cracks are showing in the crypt for the colony of Güell.

There are several reasons for this. The first one is that gravity is not the only force that buildings have to deal with. There is wind as well. Apart from that the ground that supports buildings cannot be trusted to stay in the same condition for ever, nor can mortar. Some parts shift away slowly and for buildings as fragile as Gaudí's local deviations can lead to cracks.

parameter that is determined by the stiffness of the chosen material, I is the 'moment of inertia' (which sounds complicated, but solely depends on the geometry of the strut's cross section) and L is the strut's length. The length is crucial. A short strut will be crushed under maximum load, but the longer it is the bigger the chance that buckling will take over. Over a certain length the strut or sheet will always buckle. Euler's formula works under the assumption that the strut is free to hinge at both ends. Things change if one or both ends are restrained from rotating. As a matter of fact if both ends are clamped rigidly, the maximum load will be four times higher. This does not imply that a rigid fit is the best solution. Tightly fixed structures may introduce inaccuracies – such as a slight curvature – that actually will transform buckling risk into a mere bending problem. According to Gordon this is the reason masts are no longer attached to both the deck and the keel.

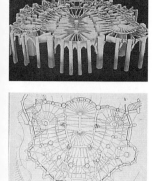

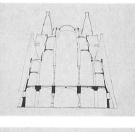

'Thickness of structural elements introduces the risk of bending and shear stresses.'

The second reason is that, although tension may be the theoretical opposite of compression, crooked columns are not the exact mechanical counterparts of funicular models. Whereas string can withstand tension stresses virtually independent of its cross section and proportions, a slender stone construction may give in to compression. Because of the thickness of stone support structures pressure forces are in some instances turned into bending. Bending leads to tension stress in certain areas and stone and cement cannot deal with that. Still Gaudí comes as close to solving the problem of compression as we'll ever be. <

See 'in depth' for more information.

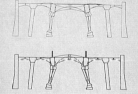

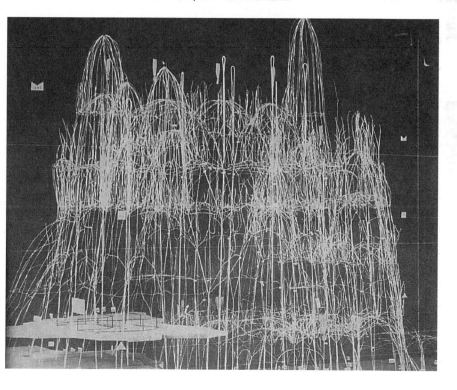

After the discovery of some cracks in Gaudi's crypt, structural computer analysis showed that the incompleteness of the building (originally it was supposed to support several higher floors) caused bending stresses. It is not expected that the cracks will result in an architectural disaster.

smart
by
Julian Vincent
nature

There is a duality between engineering and nature which is based on minimum use of energy. This is because animals and plants, in order to survive in competition with each other, have evolved ways of living and reproducing using the least amount of resource. This involves efficiency both in metabolism and optimal apportionment of energy between the various functions of life. A similar situation obtains with engineering, where cost is usually the most significant parameter. It seems likely, then, that ideas from nature, suitably interpreted and implemented, could improve the energy efficiency of our engineering at many levels. This transfer of technology, variously called bionics, biomimetics or biognosis, should not be seen so much as a panacea for engineering problems as a portfolio of paradigms.

In nature, shape is cheaper than material. This has been shown a number of times and is manifested in the remarkably high performance, both absolute and specific, of biological materials (wood is one of the most efficient of materials; antler bone is tougher than any man-made ceramic composite) which is achieved not by the use of high performance components but by the degree of detail and competence in their design and construction. The implication is not only that animals and plants have to work hard to win the raw materials – sugars, amino acids, salts – from their environment, but that their control over the assembly and shaping of these materials is much more complete than ours. An essential part of this control is the cellular feed-back mechanisms which direct the accretion of material to places where it is most needed, resulting in adaptive structures. The shape of a tree is the history of the forces which were acting on it while it grew. These same sensory mechanisms, allied to a more mobile effector system as found in animals, lead on to structures whose lightness and apparent fragility are made robust by the ability to adapt shape and structure quickly to changing loads. This adaptiveness not only reduces the energy input into the production of the structure, but also allows it to adapt to changing forces and circumstances during its lifetime, many of which may be unpredictable. Such adaptiveness has also been called smart or intelligent behaviour.

The concept of Smart or Intelligent materials (and systems and structures) has been around for a number of years. A 'smart' material (or system or structure – the one word takes all) interacts with its environment, responding to changes in various ways. A simple example is photochromic glass, darkening on exposure to light. In order to be responsive to its environment a material must have structure (for example, the molecular mechanism underlying photochromic glass) and in most instances is a system since it needs a receptor or range of receptors, a central processor which can differentiate between the inputs and integrate them into a single output, and an effector. This system could be considered as a material if it were integrated within a single lump of stuff (rather than having wires going from and to the central processor) and were being used or observed in a size range at least (some-what arbitrarily) ten times larger than the size of the individual components.

Smartness can be a simple response which follows on directly and inevitably from the stimulus; or the outcome of an if-then construct in which a decision is made based on balancing the information from two or more inputs; or the ability to learn, which is probably the smartest thing of all, since learning can lead to a patterned model of the world (the brain is 'stored environment') allowing informed prediction. It can be argued that the successful organism is the one which knows what is going to happen next and that prescience is more important than smartness, or at least subsumes it.

How can smartness be implemented, and what might it do for technology? I think it's worth first comparing the design philosophy of nature with that of an engineer. Consider a robot such as might be found in a factory. It is care-fully designed so that the arms are of the correct length and stiffness for their purpose. The joints are carefully made and give the arm(s) well-defined arcs and planes of movement. Compare the animal equivalent, which has arms of undefined length and varying stiffness, joints with very well designed bearing surfaces, and arcs and planes of movement which are relatively vaguely defined. The skeleton is defined purely functionally and can have a relatively wide variety of shapes and still work properly. For instance, in learning to walk you have a general aim and make adjustments until you manage it. But everyone walks differently due to their individual technique and adaptations to their own particular design of skeleton. So the structure of a robot need be defined only in terms of its load bearing ability and the positions and places in which it needs to hold or place things. It is necessary to have very good bearings at the joints but the material and structure of the arms and other parts are far less critical. But there is no way the robot can tell where the end of its arm might be. It has to be taught by example. Move the bits of the robot to where you want them to be and let the robot remember how it did it. Such a concept would be far cheaper to produce. For 'robot', read 'any sort of machine or structure'. The important point is that you don't have to engineer every part of the structure to very high tolerance if the structure is smart and can learn how to cope functionally with what it is.

The concepts of robotics can be applied to buildings, making them mechanically adaptive. This is already done in a relatively primitive way to give some protection against earth movements. But a truly responsive building would be prestressed, converting compressive loads into tensile ones, gathering all the residual compressive loads into a single mast. It would then respond to changes in internal and external forces by adaptively changing its state of prestress, giving lightweight stability. The technology for implementing such designs is with us, at least in 'bolt-on' mode. Piezoelectric elements can provide strain sensing and small-scale actuation, as can strain gauges and linear motors. Integration of input and output is a trivial problem with modern technology, although precisely what action might be taken in response to a given input is not always obvious.

Nature's technology involves miniaturization and integration. Sensing necessarily occurs at the molecular level. Sensitivity is much higher – in the campaniform sensillum of insects, for instance, nanometre displacements can be registered. The sensillum is integrated into the fibrous composite material which makes the exoskeleton of the insect in such a way that it can transmit displacements to the sensor cell, without compromising the mechanical continuity of the exoskeleton. This gives a model for strain sensors which could be built into a composite skin such as is used in fighter aircraft to form the basis of a health monitoring system or form part of a smart control and feedback system. The UK Defence community is also working on a reconfigurable aerofoil whose material is based on the design of the skin of the sea cucumber. This skin is a fibrous composite material (collagen in a mucopolysaccharide matrix) which can change its stiffness. Thus it can soften, change its shape, and stiffen again. The actuation system for the aerofoil could be based on another current project – worms. This involves a gel inside a suitably engineered compliant container with properly designed fibre orientations in the wall. The gel can be stimulated chemically (or electrically or thermally), change its volume by absorbing a solvent, and change its shape as a function of the geometry of its enclosure. Quite large forces can be generated in this way (plants lift concrete slabs using the same mechanism), yet the specific gravity of the system is only 1.

The ultimate smart structure would design itself. Imagine a bridge which accretes material as vehicles move over it and it is blown by the wind. It detects the areas where it is overstretched (taking into account a suitable safety factor) and adds material until the deformation falls back within a prescribed limit. We have the technology to detect the overload, but lack the means to add material automatically. We are part-way there with Carolyn Dry's self-repairing concrete structures, in which fractures cause reinforcing material to be released from embedded brittle containers and added to the structure. The ideal would be for the material to be added from an external source so that the structure was not compromised by having to contain its own salvation, necessarily reducing its load-bearing ability. Combine this with adaptive prestressing and the ability to remove material from areas which are underloaded, and we have a truly adaptive architecture.

This approach would result in lighter and safer structures, since stress concentrations would never occur, and the safety factor could be reduced as the structure reached its design optimum – registered as a reduction in the rate of internal reorganization. The paradigm is our own skeleton.

Nature is smart – are we smart enough to learn its lessons?

Nature as
a role model

The X-ray of a human femur and the Mathematical Bridge at Queen's College in Cambridge show a striking resemblance in the arrangement of stress trajectories.

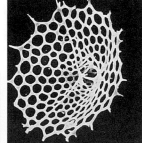

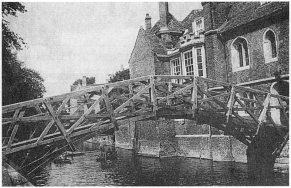

Energy and matter have to come to terms with each other. After all that is what nature is about. Structures have to compensate for omnipresent forces: intrinsic molecular forces and built-in stresses, as well as extrinsic forces encompassing all environmental influences, such as gravity and the effects of temperature and moisture. This holds true for everything dead or alive and it should therefore be a starting point for man-made constructions as well as anything else. 'Structure in nature suggests that there must be some fundamental principles and laws, an intrinsic force system, which can form the basis for the design of minimum inventory/maximum diversity building systems', says Peter Pearce in his book 'Structure in nature is a strategy for design'. Even the most complex minimum energy structure in the end is based on the force system and the principle that the triangle appears to provide us with. If you make a triangle by attaching three

'Ideally structures should be able to sweat out their skeleton at the interfaces between different kinds of matter.'

RADIOLARIA

They live all over the ocean at different depths. They can't propel themselves and float around. Most species are solitary. Of one group of species, the Spumellaria, some live in globular colonies connected by strands and enclosed within a translucent envelope. Radiolaria vary in size between 0.03 and 2 mm in diameter. Although one celled organisms, they have an intriguingly complex anatomy that has puzzled biologists since the beginning of the eighteenth century. Most knowledge of these minute beings was acquired around the year 1900.

The substance of which Radiolaria consist, is divided in a central mass and a peripheral layer of cytoplasm, separated from each other by a membrane. The outer layer often involves an envelope of bubbly little cavities and a corona of protuberances. Particularly the Spumellaria carry a gelatinous coat around the central cytoplasm mass. Many species possess a fine skeleton that makes Radiolaria stand out among other one-celled creatures. It consists of amorphous silica, which is in fact a type of glass. In this they differ from their relatives, the Acantharia, that have an often more massive strontium sulfate 'bone structure'. The silica structure in Radiolaria is totally enclosed within the outer layer of cytoplasm. The wall contains hexagonal pores that may have rounded outlines because of silica deposition.

The major fossil group of Radiolaria are the polycystines that can in their

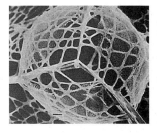

turn be divided into the Nassellaria and the afore-mentioned Spumellaria. The former usually are characterized by axial symmetry and latticed walls. The latter are spherical and have radial spines sticking out. Their skeleton often consists of two or more concentric spheres connected by bars. The refined structure cannot help but be inspiring. Among others the German architect Frei Otto is known to have based some of his designs on the Radiolaria skeleton.

In the late nineteenth century speculation started on the way in which the skeleton is formed. Haeckel presumed in 1887 that it evolved from the solid geometry of closely packed membranous surfaces. Nowadays it is assumed that shells are formed consecutively in the outer layer of the expanding cytoplasm. The skeletal growth is centrifugal in nature. This would account for stretching the silica structures, which forces them into its minimum-length hexagonal division.

Hexagonal patterns occur when structures have to absorb two-dimensional stress in all directions. Bottom: The foundation of a gigantic concrete Norwegian oil rig, here shown upside down, is built in a hexagonal pattern to maximize its ability to distribute forces.

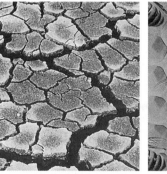

equally sized wooden bars together with hinges at the ends, the resulting structure is totally rigid. Polyhedra that can be deconstructed into triangles, can be made just as stiff. The only ones that possess this property are the tetrahedron, the octahedron (with eight angles) and the icosahedron (twenty angles). All the others cannot stand up to gravity. Triangles are the building elements of trusses and space frames.

Imagine that the hinges of the triangle are circles, large enough to just touch one another. The three circles have a fixed position among themselves. This triangular pattern can be repeated endlessly. Now suppose that the circles are pushed together slightly, from all sides; this will result in flattening the touching curves: the circles will gradually turn into hexagons.

This arrangement is omnipresent in nature. It is the

TENSEGRITY: IT'S ALIVE!

There is mutual understanding between biology and technology. Designers can get their inspiration from nature and have done so for ages. It can also be the other way around. Those who are specialized in the study of nature derive theories from ideas proposed by engineers and architects.

A splendid example of the latter is pathologist Donald Ingber who published an article in Scientific American called 'The architecture of life'. As an undergraduate at Yale University in

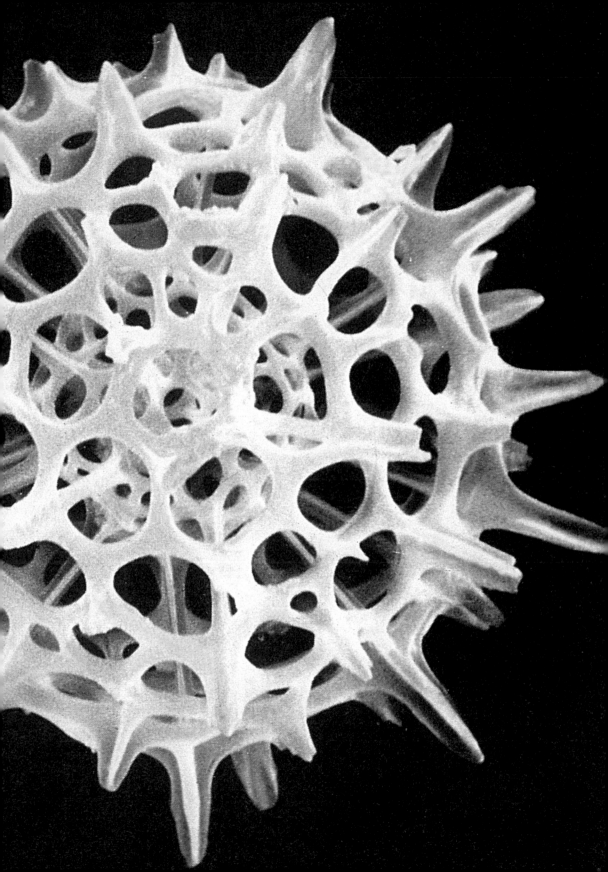

'The good kitchen uses poverty as an inspiration. Technology should do the same.'

the mid-1970s he got interested in the fact that 'tensegrity structures are mechanically stable, not because of the strength of the individual members but because of the way the entire structure distributes and balances mechanical stresses.' The tensegrity principle of tension being continuously transmitted across all structural members (every stress change in one member is shared between all of them) locally compensated by compression absorbing elements, appears to be applicable to living creatures. Mammals have muscles and tendons to distribute tension and are helped by compression absorbing bones. According to Ingber, individual cells define their shape in just the same way. It occurred to him that the mystery of a cell becoming more spherical when affixed to a thin layer of rubber and puckering the rubber substrate, could be explained if the cell was regarded as a tensegrity structure. Research seems to acknowledge this hypothesis. The cell's 'cytoskeleton' consists of contractile micro fila-

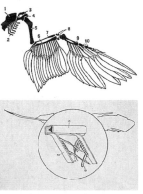

A bird's wing is a tensegrity structure. The cross-section of a feather is 'pre-buckled' to provide bending elasticity.

ments that pull its membrane and internal constituents towards the nucleus. There are two antagonists: the matrix outside the cell, and strong tubes ('micro tubules') inside it that function as girders. Tension elements and compression elements are linked by a structure of intermediate filaments. 'Although the cytoskeleton is surrounded by membranes and penetrated by viscous fluid, it is this hard-wired network of molecular struts and cables that stabilizes cell shape.' However, some cells succeed in changing their shape without the possession of internal micro

result of forces that influence matter from all sides in two dimensions. According to Pearce it can be shown that connecting an arbitrary number of random points in a plane 'in such a way as to minimize the total distance between the points results in a series of line segments meeting in threes at 120 degrees within the area defined by the point array.' This defines it as a minimum energy structure. Bees build honeycombs because they're busy being lazy. The honeycomb pattern can be perceived in the dried clay land as the result of cracking along the shortest distance. Insect's eyes and wings, giraffe and pineapple skin, the cross section of metal crystals and even of bananas:

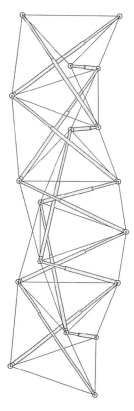

girders. When they flatten, the micro filaments appear to rearrange themselves around the nucleus into a triangular structure that strongly resembles Buckminster Fuller's geodesic dome. Ingber got to suspect this kind of behaviour experimenting with soda-straw models of cells. His suspicions were confirmed by observations in the US and Germany.
Ingber: 'It is possible that fully triangulated tensegrity structures may have been selected through evolution because of their structural efficiency – their high mechanical strength using a minimum of materials.'

they are all hexagons. Matter apparently shapes itself into the sort of structure that is best fit to absorb stress. Man has mimicked the principle in numerous variations of honeycomb materials, such as corrugated cardboard and sandwich panels with an aluminum honeycomb inside, covered with foil or sheet. Also extra strong paper made out of aramid fibres is applied in these structures.

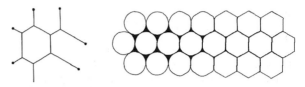

Hexagons may evolve from stretching a plane in all directions. The surface does not have to be flat, as the pineapple shows us. It can also be shaped into a spherical form. This is what happens in Radiolaria. There are at least 4000 species of these remarkable sea organisms and they all have a beautiful little skeleton with a hexagonal structure. Well, not entirely. Some polygons have fewer than six sides and others have more. A closed sphere made entirely out of a system of hexagons, regular or irregular, is mathematically impossible. If the circles in the basically triangular pattern are turned into spheres and we put a layer of the same spheres on top of them, they will stabilize their positions in the spaces between the spheres of the bottom layer, provided those are held together in some way. On top we can put a next layer, and so on. The arrangement that results is called closest packing. It is the fundamental arrangement of atoms in metal crystals and of tennis balls in a basket and it leads us to the three-dimensional counterparts of hexagonal structures.

All the spheres find themselves surrounded by 12 others. This suggest that pressed together the balls will turn into twelve-sided shapes, so called rhombic dodecahedra. But as usual three dimensions involve more complications, for in a more stable state the shapes appear to have not 12, but 14 faces (eight hexagons and six squares), and each shape is surrounded by as many others. And even this

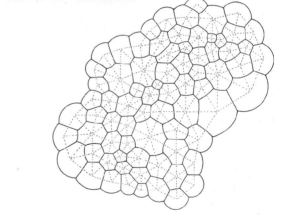

Theory shows that two-dimensional compilations of more than three bubbles are instable. Foam will always strive for minimum energy structures.

'tetrakaidekahedron' does not provide the minimum surface area in a cellular array. For this purpose all hexagon surfaces must have a slight saddle curvature. This minimum tetrakaidekahedron can be considered the theoretical basic soap bubble cell. The famous physicist Kelvin proposed it.

Nature, however, is stubborn, for this cell is rare in real everyday soap. The simple reason is that in practice many variations in circumstances occur, depending on stress, concentration of detergent, surface tension, and the fact that bubbles never originate simultaneously. Science sometimes involves ludicrous tasks. In this case a scientist called Matzke had to count soap bubbles and their faces and was thus able to establish that the average number was 13.40, including many pentagons.

From soap to foam is a small step. Just like soap, foams have cells with a range of sizes. Gibson and Ashby state in their book 'Cellular Solids' that the range can be so broad, that the largest cells are hundreds of times bigger than the smallest. Foam usually originates from gas bubbles nucleating in liquid and growing, initially as spheres. These turn into polyhedrons as they start touching each other. The resulting

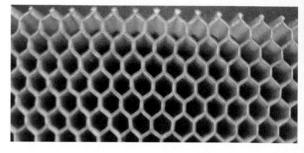

foam consists of irregular cells with 15.54 faces. Cell shape depends on competitive growth, surface tension and viscous forces, that is, if we consider a foam originating unconstrained by local forces from outside.

If for instance liquid polymer is foamed in a mould, viscous forces cause cells to elongate in the direction in which the foam moves. In bone and wood the shapes of the cells depend on the load that the cell structure has to carry. Just after 1900 in 'On Growth of Form' D'Arcy Wentworth Thomson among other things studied the morphological likeness of the femur and honeycombs. But there is an important difference: the cell walls in the human femur follow the directions of the stresses that it is subject to. If someone uses one leg

'Nature teaches us how to make large structures with minimum use of material.'

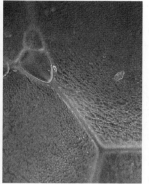

A PLASTIC SOUFFLÉ

Mixing solid material with air bubbles enhances some important properties, such as bending efficiency, thermal insulation and even flavour (crisps). To produce foam there has to be a 'blowing agent' within material that turns from solid or fluid into gas at a temperature at which the material itself is easily deformed without disintegrating. 'In situ foaming' is a treatment applied to thermoplastic film impregnated with a blowing agent. It is placed between two composite plates containing the polymer and heated in a press. When the liquid starts boiling we get foam in between the plates and they move apart as far as the press allows. Blowing agents, often chloride or fluoride based, are usually toxic. At the Laboratory of Structures and Materials in Delft a process was developed in which the blowing agent is non-toxic and – this must seem very strange – is not suitable for impregnating the amorphous plastic. It can be alcohol, or even water.

To understand how this can be achieved some knowledge of cooking is necessary. Lentils and peas for instance need to steep in water for quite some time, before they are saturated enough to be susceptible to the influence of boiling water. In this case the swelling fluid is the same as the one responsible for cooking.

Before foaming the film can be impregnated with a swelling agent, toxic as ever, but in the next stage this fluid can be displaced by a non-toxic fluid. So it is not the toxic stuff that has to be heated. The clean foams have even better quality than the toxic ones.

in a different way than the other, because of professional circumstances – bus conductors often lean on one leg when they are waiting for new passengers during the ride – this will clearly show in different femoral bone transsections.

Bone is strong and light because of its foamy substance. Foam is used in sandwich materials. There also happens to be a two dimensional derivative of naturally grown structures, such as bone. It is called the 'Michell structure'. A frame construction is able to turn a bending force into tension and compression stresses in separate bars. Depending on the way in which these are composed the construction becomes more efficient, that is lighter in relation to the load it is able to take. Though complex, the Michel structure requires the smallest amount of material. Nature shows the way to minimum energy. <

See 'in depth' for more information.

Left: Otto Lilienthal built his airplanes according to examples he saw in nature.

Length: 9,25 metres, Height: 3,05 metres,
Wingspan 11,43 metres, Maximum operating altitude: 7500 metres, Maximum
take-off weight: 1912 kilograms, Empty weight: 1128 kilograms

Extra 400

For builders of small aircrafts the jump from metal to composite is not too difficult. Together with the German company Extra Flugzeuge GmbH, located in Hünxe near the Dutch border, the Faculty of Aerospace Engineering of the University of Technology in Delft developed the Extra 400. It shows that composite materials enforce a different way of thinking about aircraft construction. The new plane has got its skeleton on the outside.

The airplane industry is on a continuous quest for lighter structures. The profit per chair is constantly decreasing while the costs are rising. Production is more expensive than it ever was. The reason is that the benefits of further improvement in metal constructions have become relatively small. Manufacturing methods have remained virtually unchanged for decades. Moreover, structures have become more vulnerable to unexpected events, fatigue and corrosion and more costly to maintain and repair. Metals airplanes have reached the top of the S-curve that describes their life cycle. It won't take long before deeper thinking in metal will cost more money than it saves.

The jump to a new S-curve is at hand. It is the only way to make improvements profitable once again. For some years modest attempts are being made to enhance the performance of large passenger carriers while reducing the production costs by switching from metal to composite materials. However, the basic construction principles usually remain unchanged. Metal is translated into fibres and plastics rather unthinkingly, without reconsidering basic structural principles. Still, the territory of composite parts is steadily growing. Whereas now new materials are commonplace in tail parts, ailerons and

COMPOSITE AIRCRAFT

Some composite airplanes are already on the market. The first one appeared in 1989. It is the canard modelled (the stabilizers are at the front instead of the tail) Beech Starship. It is a small turboprop driven business craft that can carry up to eight passengers. Unlike the Extra 400 its fuselage has a circular transsection, which simplifies the pressure cabin's sandwich structure.

Composite is not uncommon in military aircraft. The B2 Spirit by Northrop Grumman is a long-range stealth bomber. It has an aluminum and titanium

load bearing internal structure and 80 percent of the body is made out of composite materials, which in their turn consist of carbon or glass fibres and several thermosetting resins. A special machine was developed for automatic lamination of stiffeners. Composite parts are one third lighter than they would have been in metal and considerably more durable. Moreover they are better

The first Beech business aircraft (above) has a staggeringly beautiful advanced aerodynamic shape that nonetheless is made out of steel tubes and linen. Beech's Starship, recognizable through its canard concept (below), was the first full composite airplane.

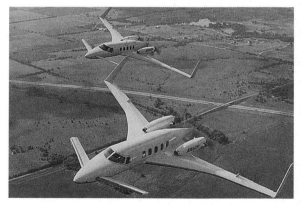

resistant to fatigue.
Because of this the B2
features a high payload
and a phenomenal radius
of action. Its shape is
special. The fuselage and
wings have almost
become one. This may be
the basic principle for airplanes to come, as it is a
way to rule out structural
discontinuities.
A property of composite
materials that has not
been mentioned yet is
their ability to be tailored
according to special
needs. By manipulating
mutual directions of
fibres, elastic behaviour
can be controlled. It is
possible to design a
structure that changes its
shape in an 'abnormal'
way under the influence

flaps, they will no doubt be used to produce entire
wings and fuselage sections in the near future.
Helicopters, military aircraft, gliders and small aircraft,
such as the Extra 400, are already being made entirely
out of composites. The most important argument is
enhancement of the price/performance ratio. Moreover
the jump to the fresh S-curve is easier because the
parts are smaller which makes investments in processing equipment, such as curing ovens, much less drastic.
The most important advantage in comparison with
metal constructions is integration of functions. Less
parts are needed. Assembly of small composite airplanes is not unlike gluing a plastic scale model together.
For larger planes the development of new constructive
concepts and production technologies is crucial. A
solution may be found in assembling sandwich constructions that consist of fibre-reinforced polymers
made by means of in situ foaming. Curing fuselage and
wings of, for instance, wide body aircraft in gigantic
pressurized ovens wouldn't make much sense.
Function integration is the starting point for composite
airplanes. Therefore current design practice has to
change. As it is, it is characterized by a sequence of
optimizing activities. First strength and stiffness are
optimized and after the structural problems are solved
physical constraints, such as thermal and acoustic
insulation, are dealt with by adding absorbing blankets
and foams. All this is detrimental to lightness and
costs. In the new situation the extra functionality will
evolve almost automatically from materials and construction. Stiffness and sound insulation are part of the
same deal, especially in the case of sandwich composites.
An important characteristic of materials is their structural efficiency: their ability to withstand deformation in
relation to their density. In the two skins of sandwich

of forces in order to perform a certain function.
Windmill blades for
instance can be designed
in such a way that they
undergo a functional
change by the centrifugal
forces that occur at a certain speed. They cause
the volution to diminish,
thereby slowing the mill
down.
The principle of elastic
tailoring is also used in
the X-29 first strike fighter by Northrop Grumman.
It is also a canard air-
plane and its specialty is
that the arrow of the
wings points backwards.
Because of this the fighter is more efficient and
better manoeuvrable.

Ray fish shapes lead the way for
future airplane development. The fully
composite B2 Spirit (top left) may
have set an early example.
Wings don't necessarily have to point
backward, as long as composite
design compensates for deformations,
like in the X-29 (above).

'Reducing the weight of isolated airplane parts may lead to a counterproductive increase of its overall weight.'

materials this factor largely depends on specific stiffness. Carbon fibre skins appear to be the best choice for sandwich constructions dominated by compression, tension and bending. Aluminium and steel perform almost as well.

This is where an important construction feature of composites comes in sight. It evolves from the trinity of shape, material and process: doubly curved and durable sandwich constructions are much easier to produce with composite skins than they are with metal ones. The disadvantage of composites is their relative brittleness. They are unforgiving when designers make mistakes that cause stress concentrations, usually on spots where different parts meet, or where a hole or cut-out in the structure is necessary. Metals are 'wiser' in this respect because of their local plasticity. Fortunately the Extra 400 sandwich concept allows easy prevention of this kind of fault. For one thing it has built in stiffness and doesn't need additional elements that would lead to the risky business of introducing unforeseeable stresses. Moreover sandwich materials can be composed in such a way that they serve as thermal and acoustic isolators. Therefore

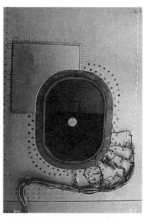

Measuring stress around the cut-out for a window.

HOLE IN THE WALL

Holes in walls, or rather the stress they cause, can be made to virtually disappear, provided the walls consist of the right sandwich material. Overpressure in a monolithic cylinder with a round hole in it will result in stress concentrations around the hole.
Holes, cracks and sharp corners in otherwise regular shapes may in Gordon's words 'raise the local stress very dramatically indeed.' Stress in a way behaves like a flow of force transfer. The effect of stress concentration can be compared to, for instance, four lanes of traffic that at a certain point along the way have to move down

to two, because a truck carrying chickens has overturned. The same number of cars have less space at their disposal, like the forces. It is why slabs of chocolate break easily along the grooves. The stress increase depends on the curvature parameter μ, which represents the relation between the size of the cylinder and the size of the hole.

$$\mu = \frac{\sqrt[4]{12\,(1 - \upsilon^2)}}{2} \cdot \frac{a}{\sqrt{R \cdot t}}$$

n = Poisson ratio
R = cylinder radius
a = polar coordinate circular hole
t = wall thickness cylinder

The stress distribution around the hole (only half of it is shown, 180°, because the distribution is of course symmetrical) is represented in the graph on page 64. If μ equals zero the cylinder is so wide that there is in fact no cylinder. Instead there is a flat sheet, equally strong in all directions under stress in two perpendicular directions. The figure shows that stress concentration is limited to 3. But it is easy

'Riveting is causing controlled structural damage.'

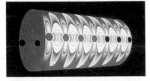

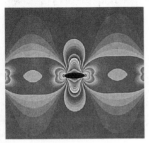

Computer simulation of stress concentrations around fuselage cut-outs.

to see that it quickly rises with an increasing µ.
If the cylinder is made out of sandwich material vast improvements are possible, for which only little core material is necessary. Even a thin layer of core material already reduces stress concentrations almost to the level of flat sheet. Sandwiching is easy, for in calculations a pressurized cylinder may be treated as if it were a flat sheet under tension stress.

chances are that sandwich materials with foam cores and carbon fibre reinforced polymers own the future. The Extra 400 is designed to fly at altitudes for which a pressure cabin is needed. Air pressure inside is higher than outside. The small plane's functionality demands that the transsection is not circular, which happens to be the natural shape for inflated objects. This implies that the sandwich shell structure will be subject to bending forces.
In the preliminary phase the choice for the skin had fallen on epoxy resin, reinforced with glass fibres, on the basis of cost and experience. Extra Flugzeuge is already familiar with the technology of laminating by hand, followed by vacuum bagging and curing. The chosen epoxy system is widespread and certified. All changes in material application are hard and costly in the aviation industry. Certification to improve safety obviously can be considered to slow down technical

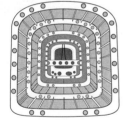

The structural difference between a classic metal fuselage (above) and a composite pressurized cabin.

stress distribution around a hole in a pressurised monolytic cylinder

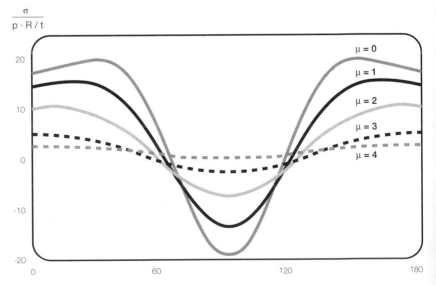

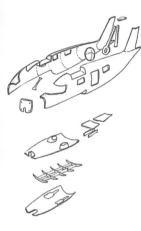

THE FULL PROCESS
Like any other product development process airplane design involves a constant quest to find the optimum balance between added value and competitiveness. An extra feature is worthless if it is too expensive. On the other hand the customer wants to get the most for his money. Designing an airplane, however, is extremely complex. Airplane development starts with an extensive pre-design stage in which the general requirements are established: payload, size, cruise speed, stability, etcetera. These are translated into a broadly outlined solution, which nowadays is usually represented in a computer model that is refined along the way.

It is not until the general proposal is finished that the design process really starts. All kinds of characteristics have to be measured against the possibilities of realization. Producibility may for instance be enhanced by integration of more functions into one part. But this process may turn out to be unfeasible, because the initial number of air-

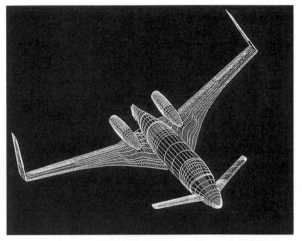

planes to be produced may be too low.

Every airplane should be able to help its passengers survive as well as it can. Composites have excellent impact resistance and damage and fatigue tolerance, provided part integration and geometrics are optmized. Thermal and acoustic insulation need to be investigated thoroughly, like all the other properties, all the way from structural behaviour and flying characteristics to the placement and shape of control buttons in the cockpit. An aircraft consists of thousands of parts. Prototyping is crucial to get to know their

quality. Since a computer is nothing but a virtual container full of assumptions, testing the real thing is the only way to find out if the design performs according to preset requirements.

'The Extra 400's external skeleton provides it with the same kind of structural integrity that Radiolaria have.'

with the plane's aerodynamic properties. Because of the pressure the composite belts wouldn't even have to be glued to the fuselage. Body stress levels have been chosen in order precisely to prevent instable growth of damage in case of a mishap.

Stress concentrations caused by the cut-outs are compensated by the structure itself. The window pans made out of light composite don't have to do anything stressful. Their only task is to keep the windows in place. The solution is simple because of the intrinsic bending stiffness of sandwich materials. <

improvement. On the basis of structural efficiency glass fibres were changed into carbon, as it delivers the same rigidity at one third of the skin weight.

As bending forces are dominant because of the pressure inside the cabin, avoidance of stress concentrations is crucial for the Extra 400 to be successful. The same holds true for peel-off loads – the kind whereby one element is torn loose from the other along the touching surface, like removing sticky tape. Around windows and doors stiffeners are essential to compensate for the loss of integrity caused by the cut-outs. The Extra 400's most interesting feature is that the stiffeners are on the outside of the fuselage like belts. The skin is draped against the skeleton from the inside. This makes the aircraft the proud owner of an embedded external skeleton, just like Radiolaria. It is the only logic solution as the pressure forces the sandwich skin into the stiffeners, whereas in aluminium pressure cabins the skin is riveted or glued on the outside of the frames, thus causing peel-off stress and additional bending in some frame areas. This is where a very important advantage of external fibre reinforced plastic stiffeners comes in handy: they can be shaped and embedded in such a way that they won't interfere

THE FINAL TRIAL

A cat will never jump on ice. It will always first make sure that it holds. People do this too, especially if they live in Friesland, in the northern part of the Netherlands. Almost every Dutch winter has frost periods and whenever the temperature has remained below zero Celsius for a week or so, newspapers start speculating on the chances of an 'Elfstedentocht', a 200 kilometre skating tour through eleven Frisian towns. Testing and repairing the ice, which must be about 12 centimetres thick, determines if this national event will take place. The example shows a slight difference between cats and people. Cats use themselves as a criterion to judge ice or a tree branch, and mankind has learned to use objective standards. The more people are involved in the use of the test object, the more standardized tests will become. A Mini fitted with a steering mechanism on back wheels three metres behind the actual car body served to check whether the back steering principle would be safe to break the sound barrier with a unique car meant for a specialized driver. On the other hand prototypes for every mass produced car have to pass a great number of standard tests,

'In civil aviation a considerable volume of corrosive moisture condensates on the inside metal skin of airplanes. Composites are better insulators.'

even evading a virtual moose.
Testing prototypes and real models is the only way to see if theories really work. A biologist builds a model of a one celled organism with plastic drinking straws to check if tensegrity is involved, and an archaeologist organizes the manual reconstruction of Stonehenge with concrete blocks. Engineering and design involve a succession of many simple and complicated experiments. Testing itself is also subject to trial and error and improvement. The extras that used to populate airplane wings and car roofs have now been replaced by computers and machines that extensively simulate practical circumstances and scenarios .

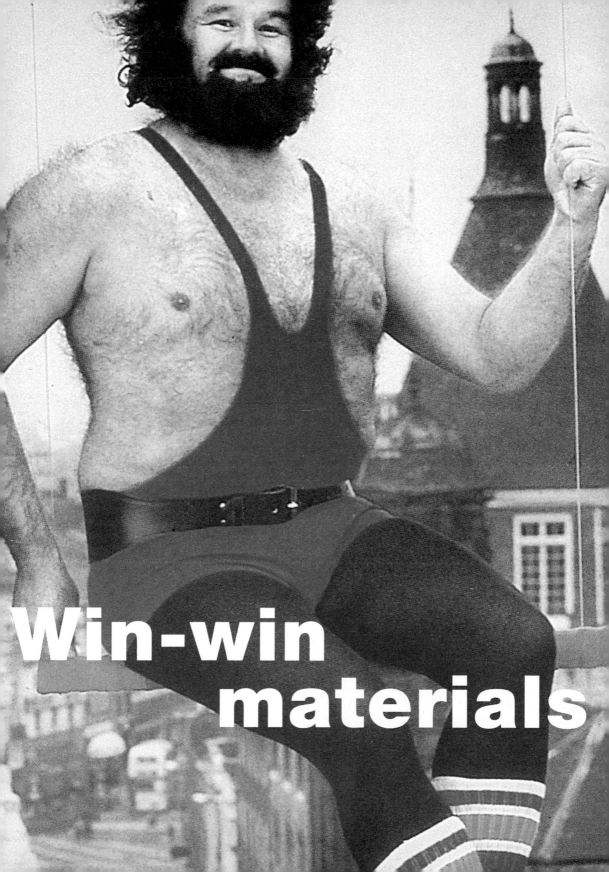

Win-win
materials

Nowadays composites are generally looked upon as compounds of polymers and other substances. However, the principle of combining materials to create new ones doesn't necessarily involve plastics. Composites probably came into being just after mankind originated and they can be any combination of usually two kinds of materials: elements, usually different in nature, and an encapsulating matrix. The result is a material that features the best of both. Essentially there are four basic groups: wood and

The strength, stiffness and impact resistance properties of high quality composites are provided by continuous fibres. The main ones are aramid (previous page) carbon (above), and glass (left).

'Introduction of new composites is not impeded by their properties, but by traditional production methods.'

COMPETING WITH METAL

We can make a simple comparison between metals and composites with the help of their material efficiency (m.e.) for structures that may suffer from bending and buckling. This characteristic depends on two basic material properties: density (ρ) and Young's Modulus (E), which expresses the ratio between stress and the resulting elastic deformation. Its alternative name is Elasticity Modulus, hence the abbreviation E. Not all materials perform the same way in identically stressful circumstances. That is why material efficiency is related to the type of stress and construction that the material is used in.

To simplify the comparison and still present a broad insight into different material characteristics we shall look at beams, sheets and shells under compression, tension, buckling and bending. In the case of sandwich panels we shall do the same, but leave out the bending stresses. All in all this provides us with three versions of material efficiency:

Version A applies to solid beams, sheet and shells, as well as sandwich panels in tension and pure compression:

$$me_A = \frac{E}{\rho}$$

Version B applies to solid beams in compression, buckling and bending:

$$me_B = \frac{\sqrt{E}}{\rho}$$

Version C applies to solid sheet and shells in compression, buckling and bending.

$$me_C = \frac{\sqrt[3]{E}}{\rho}$$

We can calculate the m.e.'s for two common construction metals, aluminium and the kind of steel used in cars, and for three bidirectional laminates (the fibres are arranged perpendicular to one another) containing 50 percent epoxy resin. For beams, sheet, shells and sandwich panels that are critical under tension or compression, usually in slender constructions, we see that both metals offer attractive solutions, even more so because manufacturing technologies are both mature and cheap. Only carbon fibre reinforced epoxy resin can do better, but affordable production of the described structures may be difficult. If beams are predominantly bent or compressed – this is what they have to live through as stiffeners or elements in the truss structure of for instance a space frame, carbon is superior to metals, shortly followed by aramid. We also see that glass reinforced epoxy disappoints. This is why it never could compete successfully against aluminium. This holds true for the third column as well. Solid plates and shells under bending or compression stress, such as we may find in all kinds of vehicles, are preferably made out of resin with carbon or aramid fibres in it. Considering the trinity concept the conclusion is that production process development is paramount for composites.

other renewables such as straw or bamboo, plastics, glass and ceramics, and metals. Pure carbon is hard to allocate to one of these groups – it occurs both in polymers and in renewables – so we'll add it as a fifth. Composites usually are a combination of materials out of each group, in order to create the required synergy. In theory we can cook up ten possible combinations, but in daily practice six are in use.

Reed without a trace of matrix material, but bundled and shaped in the most obvious way, is used to build ultra light swamp huts.

elastic properties of some fibres, natural composites and steel compared

material		density ($10^3 \cdot$ kg / m^3)	Young's modulus ($10^9 \cdot$ N / m^2)	Yield stress ($10^6 \cdot$ N / m^2)	Yield strain (%)	elastic energy/weight (J / kg)
steel	0.2 carbon quenched	7.8	210	773	0.2	99
	piano wires/springs	7.8	210	3100	0.8	1590
animal	bovine bone	2.1	22.6	- 254	- 1.4	846
	ivory	1.9	17.5	217	1.2	685
	buffalo horn	1.3	2.65	- 124	- 3.2	1530
	sinew	1.3	1.24	103	4.1	1620
hardwood	birch	0.65	16.5	137	1.0	1050
	Wych elm	0.55	10.9	105	1.0	950
	ash	0.69	13.4	165	1.0	1196
	oak	0.96	13.0	97	1.0	703
	elm	0.46	7.0	68	1.0	740
softwood	scots pine	0.46	9.9	89	0.9	870
	taxus brevifolia	0.63	10.0	116	1.3	1100
natural organic polymer base fibers	jute	1.46	10-25	400-800	1-2	
	flax	1.54	40-85	800-2000	3-2.4	
	sisal	1.33	46	700	2-3	
	hemp	1.48	26-30	550-900	1-6	
	coir	1.25	6	221	15-40	
	cotton	1.51	1-12	400-900	3-10	
synthetic organic polymer base fibers	HM-Carbon (M40)	1.83	392	2740	0.7	
	HT-Carbon (T300)	1.76	230	3530	1.5	
	HM-Aramide	1.45	133	3500	2.7	
inorganic base fibers	S/R-Glass	2.48	88	4590	5.4	
	E-Glass	2.58	73	3450	4.8	

note 1: Northern hardwoods, sinew and horn are the basic structural materials for laminated composite bows and chariots from Mesopotamia and Egypt.
note 2: Taxus baccata is used for the medieval longbows.
note 3: Horn, a natural thermoplastic polymer was especially applied in the compression loaded areas.
note 4: Sinew, superior in tension, was applied for strings and bow-reinforcement; more in general it was used as a shrinking (smart) robe to encapsulate and to connect different components.
note 5: Properties of natural materials are very variable, the figures shown are most averages in tension or compression (-) and collected from many different publications.
note 6: Yield stress is the lowest stress at which a material undergoes plastic deformation or failure.

MAKING ENDS MEET
Every structure comes to an end sooner or later. We're talking about ends and edges. That is where design usually becomes difficult. The edge needs a fine finish or worse: one end has to be fastened to another. This may consists of the same material, or be of a different nature. Edges and joints are complex issues in the world of composites. More than on anything else structural efficiency depends on joints. It is a blessing in disguise that composites often allow elimination of joints by functional integration. They even can simply be evaded. Recently the American Quadrax Corporation acquired a

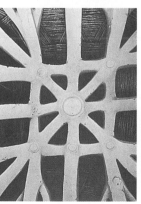

Ceramic substances may serve as a matrix for straw or bamboo. They are used in building technology. With metal inside they form a common combination, exemplified by probably the crudest composite of all: reinforced concrete. There are, however, more refined variations. The four others indeed all involve synthetic organic materials. Evidently plastics are fond of teamwork. Laminated with wood they probably are the oldest kind of advanced composites. In early times wood was glued to materials of animal origin such as sinew and horn, which – few people know this – behave like synthetic thermoplastics. They soften when heat is applied to them. These days wood is still laminated with polymers. Formica for instance consists of layers of wood with one layer of phenolic plastic on top, and modern bows for archery feature wooden limbs laminated with fibre reinforced resins. Plastics can also be combined with metals in several ways. But the most common combination is made with ceramics, glass and several kinds of fibres.

Clay is an excellent building material, but its building quality improves in combination with reed. The humble wattle-and-daub roof construction, as seen during its construction as well as from the inside after finishing it, must have evolved in elaborate gothic structures over centuries.

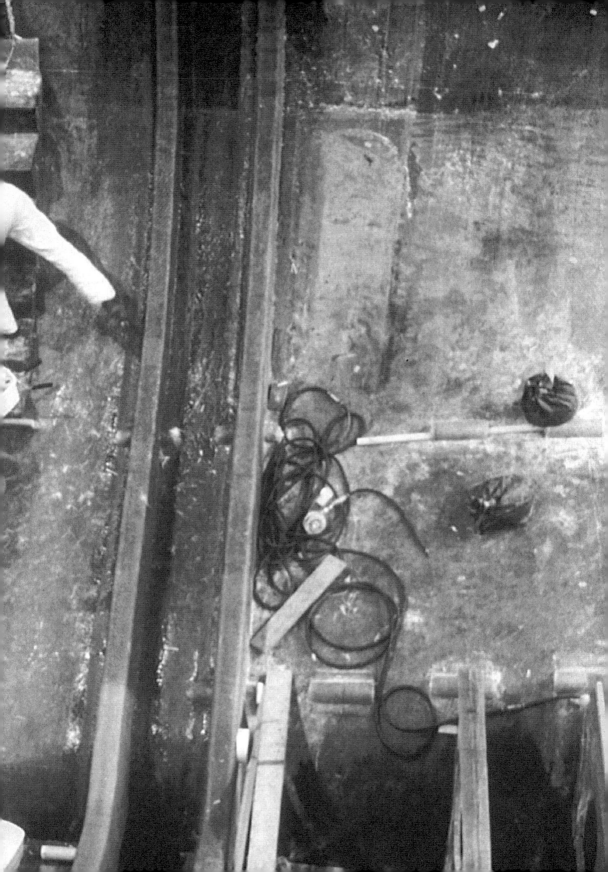

patent on a circular loom to braid composite tape (parallel fibres embedded in plastic) in a circle. Ironically this braiding technique is just about as old as the principle of the braided basket. Strength and stiffness in composites are determined by the arrangement of fibres. This has to be established in accordance with the size and location of joints, after which the composition and dimensions of the composite structure in between have to be dealt with. Moreover fibre-reinforced composites are brittle in comparison with metals. Whereas metals are able to yield to forces, so as to minimize stress concentrations, compos-

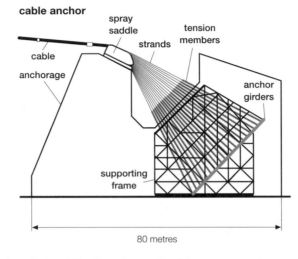

cable anchor

spray saddle

cable anchorage

strands

tension members

anchor girders

supporting frame

80 metres

ites find it difficult to do this as they only deal in elastic deformation. Like most materials, composites can be joined to each other and to different materials by bolting, riveting and bonding. For high loaded structures with a thickness over some 10 millimetres mechanical fastening is the strongest solution.

For thinner composite sheet materials bonding is preferable. The joint should be designed in such a way that it is stronger than the material outside it. There are several types of joints depending on the way in which stress is trans-

ferred from one end to the other. The simplest and the weakest is the lap joint, in which one end is simply glued on top of the other. The most advanced (and most difficult to produce) are scarf joints and stepped-lap joints. They are the most efficient in transferring stress, because they exclude the possibility of peel, and stress concentrations are minimal. Fibres are the elements in composites that both determine the tension resistance and hamper their capacity to be joined. One of the most difficult problems is anchoring the ends of cables made out of carbon fibres. It is the reason why most suspension bridges have steel cables, even though carbon has a much higher

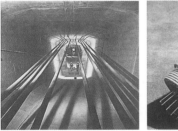

This kind of anchor at the end of a steel cable is difficult to translate into a solution for carbon cable anchoring.

This is where we have to refine the distinctions made. For one thing there are two basic groups of polymers: the already mentioned thermoplastics and thermosets. The first kind weakens under the influence of heat and the second originates from an irreversible chemical reaction. The plasticity of the latter group does not depend on temperature, within certain boundaries. Both kinds can be combined with other materials in different forms. Also both kinds can be produced in a rubbery quality, which means that they have the ability to return to their original shape after a large deforma-

'With composites the designer once more becomes the integrator of form and function.'

tion. The rubber phase occurs within a certain temperature trajectory.

Mixed with particles plastic's properties tend to improve. They can be tuned to meet the mechanical and physical requirements. Wood or glass globules make them lighter. If short pieces of glass fibre, or ceramic particles are mixed in the compound, they become stronger and gain in heat resistance. The latest development is called 'nanocomposite'. In this case the quality of plastics improves radically by adding a relatively small amount of extremely tiny clay particles. Thermoplastic composites of this mixed nature are processed in the same way as plastics without fillers: mainly by thermoforming and injection moulding. In the same way thermoset composites can be mixed and processed like ordinary thermosets. Mixing is dealt with before the shaping process, for instance in the case of spraying a mixture of polyester and short fibres in a mould.

Polymers can also serve as an impregnation for continuous fibres, that is fibres that are so long that they can be wound up on a reel. They can be positioned parallel to each other (uni-directional or UD) or processed into textiles that can consist of jute or flax, glass or carbon fibres, and of different kinds of strong synthetic fibres such as aramid or polyethylene. In the case of thermoplastics the impregnation must always take place before the forming process. This results in so called prepregs that can be shaped by heating, and consequently bending, pressing or draping. Thermosets can be used to either impregnate shaped mats that are already brought into in the acquired shape, or unshaped pieces of textile. These are also called prepregs, but they have to be cured after shaping, whereas thermoplastic prepregs only have to cool down.

The last option is lamination of different layers of

cable section

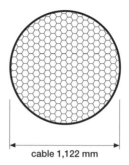

cable 1,122 mm

material efficiency and is more cost effective in the long run (no maintenance).

Steel cables feature different anchoring principles, the most common one being the hitch: the strands at the end are braided back into the body of the rope to form a loop. Cables with a diameter in the region of a metre are impossible to bend in a loop. The new Akashi Kaikyo bridge in Japan with a span of almost two kilometres, finished in April 1998, features anchors with a saddle for the main cable (1122 millimetres in diameter). At both ends the strands are spread out and fastened to a girder supported by a frame. The whole lot is cast into concrete.

Carbon is too brittle for this kind of anchoring. Recently the Swiss company EMPA suggested a solution in which the carbon cable elements are cast into a resin cone that fits into a steel counterpart. It will be applied for the first time in the Winterthur bridge to anchor the two 35 metre cables. Even carbon has to prove itself in small structures.

Recently a loom for circular braiding was patented. It can do automatically what basket makers have been doing for a long time.

prepregs right into the acquired shape. Lamination provides continuous fibre composites with a characteristic advantage: designers are in total control of tuning strength, stiffness and elastic deformation behaviour by manipulating fibre directions to optimize the way in which they behave under the influence of stress. The elastic tailoring of wings is gaining interest. Laminate failure typically occurs between layers. This tearing effect is called delamination.

Of course the mentioned modes of composition are not strictly separated. It is not uncommon to laminate fibre reinforced materials with sheet metal. They can be considered three component composites and don't become fatigued as easily as aluminium itself. The layer of reinforced resin is a difficult barrier for the progress of cracks.

Polymers are light in comparison with metals and if the combination of strength, stiffness and lightness becomes paramount, then plastics reinforced with continuous fibres offer a solution that is becoming ever more obvious. They are the ones that will have to take over from metals because of the increasing importance of lightness and their ability to take any shape.

This does not imply that they must simply replace all metals. Remember that design always evolves from the combination of shape, material and process, the famous trinity. If less material weight is the only advantage, considerable cost savings are doubtful, especially because the new composite way of thinking has to compete with thoroughly experienced metal technologies.

When aluminium arrived in the airplane industry in the early 20's the situation was totally different. Aviation itself was still in its infancy. There were no jet engines, the facts on aerodynamics or metal fatigue were hardly known, nor did we know how to properly control structures as complex as a pressure cabin with win-

THE WETTER THE BETTER

In order for polymers to be able to get attached to foreign fibres they need to have a relatively low surface tension. In general surface tension is the force that keeps it together. Everyone knows what water can do in this respect. A glass can be overfilled without spilling, and a steel needle can float on water if it is gently lowered onto the surface. Soap reduces the surface tension of water, which allows it to enter narrow openings. The glass will then overflow and the needle will sink.

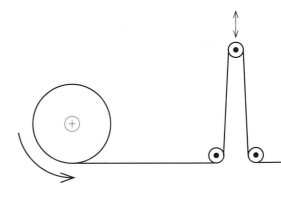

dry fiber creel   fibre tension control

'Beside excellent mechanical properties composites have physical advantages too.'

dows. So in fact the development of aluminium technology coincided with that of the entire airplane producing industry. Therefore metals had the chance to completely take over from canvas, wood and steel cables in about 20 years.

Fibre reinforced composites on the other hand will have to prove themselves against materials that thrive in a mature industry. Their idiosyncrasies are still largely unfamiliar and, although they are rapidly becoming cheaper and their properties are very promising, they're still relatively expensive. Whereas production technologies for aluminium were available in the 20's and 30's, composites are still largely processed by hand. Few industrial technologies are available, such as winding, thermoforming and in-situ foaming, which are all being developed at the Delft Faculty for Aerospace Engineering.

Moreover the current safety philosophy in aviation cannot simply be transplanted from aluminium to composites, because they react to stress and impact in a totally different way. For one thing metals undergo plastic deformation before they give in and break. Continuous fibre reinforced plastics simply don't. You can't kick a dent in a composite panel. It either remains undamaged or it breaks. <

The surface tension of a fluid relative to a thread can be observed. In the case of a low surface tension the fluid will want to spread along the length of the thread in an effort to wet it, whereas a droplet will keep itself to itself if its surface tension relative to the thread is high. For good bonding we need to tune the surface tension of polymer and thread for sufficient wetting to occur. This can be achieved by adding something to the polymer or by pre-treating fibres.

NEW HYPERFIBRE

The brittleness of carbon fibres slows down the development of new applications. Instead of adapting constructions and processes to carbon one can also try to develop new fibres. AKZO NOBEL is currently working on a new Rigid-Rod polymer by the code name M5. It is just about as strong as carbon, but less vulnerable and easier to process. M5 can easily be bonded to different matrix polymers. Experiments suggest that M5 composites may perform better than carbon reinforced polymers.

See 'in depth' for more information.

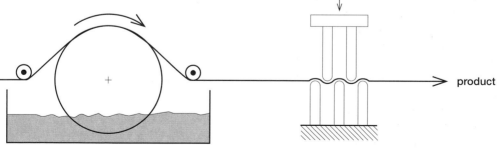

impregnation

resin content control

product

Bending for power

Warfare is fighting over power, or over what might in these cyberspace saturated times be called 'telepresence'. This is literally being present somewhere else, which in the case of war means in other people's territory, without actually being there. In an abstract sense this implies that the best way to acquire power is covering maximum distance with minimum energy. In the Old Stone age, 10,000 to 15,000 years ago, people probably did not realize this. They did, however, hunt animals and fight their enemies by hitting them with clubs and throwing stones, heavy blunt objects that took a lot of effort to handle and at the most covered distances of some tens of metres. Best results came from spears that were sharp and relatively light, thereby concentrating all throwing energy in a small point. Spears could travel at reasonable speed, and further than any stone heavy enough to cause serious wounds. Nobody knows exactly when the bow and arrow came into existence. Stone arrow heads dating back as far as 50,000 years were found in Tunisia. The oldest arrowheads that have been used on arrows with great certainty, and not on spears, date back to over 10,000 years ago.

In his 'History of Warfare' John Keegan observes a major change, that the bow and arrow brought about: 'At the beginning of the New Stone Age, however, some 10,000 years ago, there occurred a revolution in weapons technology. Four staggeringly powerful new weapons made their appearance: the bow, the sling, the dagger and the mace. The last three were refinements of weapons already in existence: the mace derived from the club, the dagger from the spear point and the sling from the bolas, the last a pair of stones covered with leather and joined by a thong, thrown to entangle the legs of deer or bison which had been herded into a killing place. The atlatl, or spear throwing

ISHI THE INDIAN
Making and shooting a composite bow requires special skills. The famous actor and amateur marksman Robert Hardy provides a remarkable illustration in his standard book 'Longbow; a social and military history'. It is the story about the native American Ishi, one of the last massacre survivors of the Yana tribe. He was taken captive in 1911 and handed over to the Department of Anthropology at the

University of California. There he was introduced to Doctor Saxton Pope, who happened to be archery instructor at the university Medical School. Pope became Ishi's student in bow making and hunting. Ishi used the outer part and the sapwood of a juniper. He scraped and rubbed it on sandstone until it had the required oval trans-section. Recurve of the limbs was acquired by bending the wood over a heated stone and after that leaving it to season, attached to a special mould. After that Ishi glued sinew from the leg tendons of deer – he first chewed them to make them soft – to the back of the bow with a compound made out of boiled salmon skins. At both ends he completely embedded the bow in sinew. After this process it was laid to dry, bound together with willow bark. A few days later the bow was finished by smoothening it and sizing the surface with more glue. The string he made out of thinner tendons from the deer's shank and arrows were cut from wych hazel and straightened by heating and bending.

The Yana Indian was not very good at target shooting. In a contest he lost with a score amounting to less than half of Pope's. But he was a far better hunter.

Hardy cites Pope, who wrote: 'In all things pertaining to the handicraft of archery and the technique of shooting, he was most exacting. Neatness about his tackle, care of his equipment, deliberation and form in his shooting were typical of him; in fact, he loved his bow as he did no other of his possessions. It was his constant companion in life and he took it with him on his last journey.' Ishi died of tuberculosis in 1916.

lever, was probably also an indirect precursor of the sling, since it worked by a simple principle. The bow, however, was a real departure. It may be seen as the first machine, since it employed moving parts and translated muscular into mechanical energy.' Indeed it did. It was the first device that allowed energy to be not just transformed, but accumulated and transferred to a light and small projectile. The bow was able to 'throw' it with much greater speed than any human arm could and the invention spread rapidly. Some consider the archer the first true warrior.

The first bows were made out of homogeneous wood, 'typically a length of sapling' according to Keegan. It must have taken thousands of years for them to evolve into very advanced composite bows, the derivatives of which are still in use in current archery practice. The composite bow is too complicated to be just an invention and it must have needed numerous years of trial and error to develop. It may have come about in the Middle East and the Far East as early as 5000 years

THE MEANING OF RECURVE

Even now, when the bow is way beyond the top of its S-curve, it is subject to study and mathematical calculations. Quite a few archery enthusiasts, professionals as well as amateurs, have made speculations on bow qualities. Recurve, shaping of the limbs in such a way that they point forward when the bow is braced, has for example been supposed to increase the string's propelling power, because it becomes effectively shorter after release. Research by Kooi and Bergman shows that this is not the case. They

ago and we know for certain from a picture on a golden bowl of that time, that it existed in 1400 BC. The shape is characterized by 'recurved' limbs. This is caused by the way in which it is strung. When it is relaxed the shape is almost like a circle. Bracing the bow, which by the way is quite difficult and takes a lot of force, counteracts this natural form: the inside of the circle becomes the front of the bow. It's 'weight', which is the amount of force it takes to fully draw the bow, can be as much as about 70 kilograms. It is reasonably accurate at 300 metres and its reach is about 700 metres. Incidentally the world record for conventional shooting (in a standing position) was set by the Turks centuries ago at 799 metres and remained unsurpassed until very recently.

The weight of the European 'longbow' is about the same. It dates from the Middle Ages and it is a far simpler weapon, usually made from yew with a wooden enforcement in the grip in the middle and horn caps at the ends of the limbs to accommodate the loops at the end of the string. Yew (Taxus Boccata) apparently is better suited to accumulate elastic strain energy than other timbers, but quickly deteriorates in hot climates. This is the reason it was mainly used in France and England, although it was imported from Spain.

The longbow has no recurve and its reach, with heavier arrows, is less than one third that of the composite bow. The main disadvantage, however, is that it cannot be shot from horseback or from a chariot, because it is too long, even longer than a person, whereas the ancient composite bow is about half that length. The lighter weight of the unfletched (featherless) arrows that were shot with it also allowed archers to carry a great many with them. They could meet the enemy with a hail of deadly needles. The composite bow reached perfection in 200 BC and didn't change until it

made a comparison between the amount of energy stored in the fully drawn bow that is available to propel the arrow, the efficiency with which this power is transferred to the arrow, and a factor that is proportional to the initial velocity.

Bows with an extreme recurve, can store by far the most energy because of their shape. On the other hand straight bows, such as the longbow are more efficient. In the end the respective initial velocities are not all that different. One could say that the structural efficiencies don't differ much.

Real differences become clear when we consider the construction of the

became obsolete as a war weapon in the last century. Keegan describes its complexity: 'It consisted of a slender strip of wood – or a laminate of more than one – to which were glued on the outer side ('belly') lengths of elastic animal tendon and on the inner side ('back') strips of compressible animal horn, usually that of the bison. The glues, compounded of boiled-down cattle tendons and skin mixed with smaller amounts reduced from the bones and skin of fish, might take more than a year to dry and had to be applied under precisely controlled conditions of temperature and humidity. A great deal of art was involved in their preparation and application, much of it characterized by a mystical, semi-religious approach.' No wonder the composite bow had to be kept in a special case when not in use, to protect it from weather influences.

The making of a composite bow started with gluing five pieces of wood together: the grip, two arms and two tips, now known as the limbs. The result was steamed into the shape of a curve, after which the horn back was glued to it to accommodate the compression strains. Then it was bent into the aforementioned circle and the tendons were glued to the inside, to what would become the bow's tension resisting face after it was braced. The composite bow can be considered a major accomplishment in the quest for power by lightness. <

sections through a turkish composite bow

black areas = horn
stippled areas = sinews
after Hein 1925

handle

limb

limb just below ear

ear

bows. Efficiency appears to depend on the difference between the mass of the arrow and the mass of the limbs. The mass of the limbs can be smaller if their ability to accumulate energy is larger, which happens to be a material property. Composite bows allow a much larger drawing weight than wooden ones in the same amount of material. Construction is what makes composite bows superior for flight shooting, propelling an arrow as far as possible.

Fake warfare

'Collision safety has very little to do with weight. What counts is the ability to absorb energy during speed reduction within a limited time trajectory.'

Part of the lightness avant-garde works in developing sports equipment. All sports articles – bats, rackets, racing cars, even skis and skates – can be traced back to either weapons, or means of transport that must have been used in warfare or hunting. The only exception is of course the ball in all its manifestations, which has its origin in the head of an enemy and in small prey animals that people played with. The golf ball's Roman predecessor was stuffed with feathers.

It is impossible to establish the exact moment when recreational sports came about. They must have started out as a peculiar mixture of military or hunting exercise and people being entertained by the cruel performance of other, less fortunate people killing each other or fighting dangerous animals. In current sports practice the lethal quality has virtually disappeared and we are left with a rather paradoxical activity, that nevertheless plays an extremely important role in modern society. No sociologist can deny that sports are associated with the social obligation of being fit and healthy, compensating as they do for the obsolescence of physical effort in transportation, work and video entertainment.

Any sport entails doing something tiring that is made difficult by arbitrary rules about what is allowed and what isn't. At the same time everybody tries to ease fitness enhancing effort by developing new concepts in

Some Indian tribes play an ancient game with a massive rubber ball

SOME HAPPY RETURNS
Contrary to popular beliefs a boomerang is not a weapon that automatically returns to the one who flings it. Some boomerangs are used for warfare and hunting and they can be thrown much further than any other piece of wood. This type of boomerang is larger, crescent-shaped, with a shallow curve. It is sometimes thrown so that it ricochets off the ground to strike its quarry. Others do return, but they are not used for wounding or killing. Still they are the most fascinating kind. According to Felix Hess, who did extensive research on the principles of boomerang flight, the shape, usually curved like a banana is not all that important for the

returning effect. Cross shapes, for instance, are used too by aborigines in the North East of Australia, but in fact almost any flat letter shaped throwing stick can return to the thrower, provided it has a wing-like cross section and is thrown in the right way. After being held by one end behind the thrower's head, the boomerang is swung rapidly over the head and thrust vertically before being released in such a way that it will start rotating. It then sweeps upward and flies, gradually turning horizontal, and often completing a circle up to 90 metres wide.

The typical behaviour of a boomerang in flight is caused by a combination of two forces: air pressure differences between the more convex side and the flatter side (which in their turn depend of the forward speed and the rotational speed), and the gyroscopic effect of the boomerang's rotation. Interestingly the dimensions of the flight don't depend on the rotational velocity, nor on the forward speed. The main ingredients for a certain path are the boomerang's weight and the lift that is provided by its profile. So the best way to throw it is determined by the boomerang rather than by the thrower.

If the effects that cause the boomerang's flight are suppressed by a complicated hub mechanism, the object will start behaving like a helicopter. In a helicopter the rotational speed and the forward velocity are important. In this case the pilot determines the flight path.

equipment design in order to improve performance. The changes in equipment usually turn out to be rather futile, for although new world records may be set, innovations are rapidly copied. In the end competition is always between athletes and not between technologies.

Not all innovations need technology. A successful change of technique may cause a jump in performance that affects an entire sports culture. In 1968 Dick Fosbury won Olympic Gold with a new backward high jump that became commonplace overnight. More recently ski-jumpers found out a way to improve their aerodynamic properties by pointing their skis outward during flight. This enlarged the average jumping distance by some ten percent.

Rules play an essential rule in technological changes. It would be pointless to ease weight-lifting or discus-throwing by applying the principle of lightness. However, where material is not part of the challenge, but a means to reach the highest speed, the deadliest ball return, or the best score, the quest for accomodating improvements can only be halted by regulations. In target archery, for instance, apart from the bow-sight, any optical device to support aiming is forbid-

The boomerang's flight path depends on its weight and the proportions of its profile. Helicopters and autogiros luckily have little in common with it.

Bamboo, originally used to make vaulting poles, is naturally divided into closed compartments that prevent it from buckling.

den. Archers that fit their bow with a lens or a small peeping hole in the string, are instantly disqualified at the beginning of tournaments. Cycle racing hasn't allowed the use of reclining bicycles since the late 30's, which has hampered further development of this type of human powered vehicle for years. Whereas the creep sensitive wooden racket has disappeared from top tennis, Major League baseball in the USA only allows the use of wooden bats. This illustrates the common practice of rules and regulations obstructing innovation.

There are no special rules for the composition of poles used for pole vaulting. From 1900 until 1942 light-weight bamboo was used. In 1957 Bob Gutowski set a world record of 4.78 metre with an aluminum pole. Don Bragg cleared 4.80 metre one year later with a steel one. The fibreglass pole, which permitted extreme flex-ion and has revolutionized vaulting technique, saw the light in the USA in 1956. The first world record using this new material was set in 1961. The Russian grand master of pole vaulting, world record holder (over 6 metres) Sergei Bubka, personally supervises the mak-ing of his poles, which involves both glass and carbon fibre reinforced plastics.

Heroes in spectacular sports draw just as much spe-cial attention as war heroes did earlier on. They are important in mass communication and represent tremendous commercial value. Top-class sport is big business. That is the reason why it is supported by sci-ence. Just like Tutankhamen had the finest craftsmen available to build his chariot - so refined that it couldn't have been done any better today - modern Formula I drivers race the best that car designers can deliver. The body of both the ancient and the modern vehicle largely consists of composite materials. They offer the advantage of lightness and the ability to be tailored

The diamond shaped frame has proven to be the lightest construction possible for metal bikes.

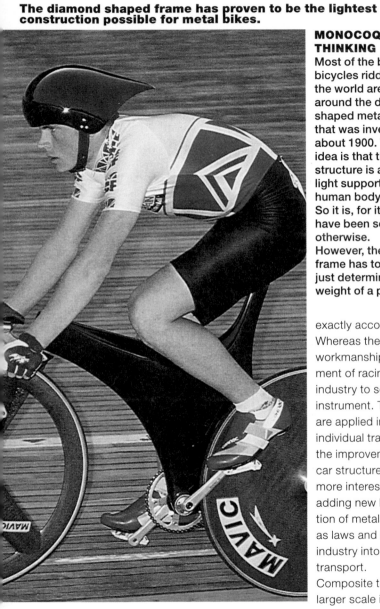

MONOCOQUE THINKING

Most of the billions of bicycles ridden all over the world are constructed around the diamond shaped metal tube frame that was invented in about 1900. The basic idea is that this kind of structure is an excellent light support for the human body.
So it is, for it couldn't have been so successful otherwise.
However, the load a frame has to take is not just determined by the weight of a person.

Left: Mike Burrows designed the Lotus carbon fibre reinforced polymer racing bicycle on which Chris Boardman shattered the world record in 1996.

exactly according to functional demands. Whereas the advanced chariot evolved from exclusive workmanship devoted to political power, the development of racing automobiles is supported by the car industry to serve as a commercial communication instrument. The inventiveness with which composites are applied in racing cars rather feeds the myth of fast individual transport than that it actually contributes to the improvement of and lightening of mass produced car structures. As for now, the car market seems to be more interested in developing the technology for adding new luxury features, than in breaking the tradition of metal car manufacturing. This is due to change, as laws and energy prices will gradually force the industry into developing lighter and safer means of transport.
Composite technologies do manifest themselves on a larger scale in the bicycle industry, albeit not always in

The dynamic torsion that she or he causes by pedalling and at the same time pulling the handlebars is just as important. This kind of force is best dealt with by a closed box construction. Such a shell can be made more cheaply in fibre reinforced polymers than in metal. The chance of structural improvement is sadly missed in the recent Dutch design for the commercially available closed 'Alleweder' (All weather) bicycle. The rider is enclosed in a protective aluminum coccoon that is riveted together according to outdated principles. Its quality is easily exceeded by the 'Cheetah', designed at Berkeley University. Its shell is made out of carbon fibre reinforced polymer. It weighs a little over 13 kilograms and set the world speed record for human powered vehicles at 111 kilometres per hour.

the right way. Manufacturers tend to simply replace metal tubing with the carbon fibre reinforced version. Sometimes they even limit themselves to coatings that resemble the carbon look. However, a magnificent example was set by the shell-framed Lotus bicycle designed by Mike Burroughs that helped set the world speed record in 1996. Since then the 'monocoque frame' is quickly becoming more accepted. Burroughs is currently developing a monocoque city bike for bicycle producer Giant. According to Burroughs light bikes have an additional advantage in that they float on water. Especially the Dutch city dweller will appreciate this quality, as hundreds, if not thousands of bicycles disappear in canals every year. <

See 'in depth' for more information.

The 'alleweder'

If labour costs become too high the product is turned into a do-it-yourself kit.

Reinventing
the wheel

Fast transportation over land takes the least energy with the use of wheels, once you've succeeded in making them. That is why they have kept on turning for ages and that is also why we still manage to modify and improve them. The use of wheels is not just a matter of being smart. It largely depends on circumstances as well. The most striking evidence for this is given to us by pre-Conquest Mexican culture.

The Aztecs did not use wheels for transportation, but they were certainly clever enough to invent the wheel – in this case possibly derived from the distaff used for thread spinning – and attach four of them to cute earthenware toy animals that kids could move about. There are two obvious reasons why the Aztecs never may have got the idea to apply this invention - which after all was thoroughly influential in the Old World - to easily move heavy loads around. To start with, they had no large strong domesticated animals, like deer, horses or oxen. Moreover they lived in a mostly mountainous region in which wheels would have been a burden rather than a blessing for transportation of goods and people. The Aztec culture simply didn't care about wheels.

Across both the oceans things were different. In Europe and China rivers accommodated transport over vast distances and where rivers were absent caravans could carry loads over vast plains. The first primitive wheeled vehicles in all probability evolved from the use of tree trunks to reduce the friction between the earth and heavy loads. There is some pictorial evidence that early wheels may have been simply thick slices of a tree trunk, some 40 centimetres in diameter and the same width, with a hole in the middle for the axle.

The first real disc wheels, however, were made out of oak planks that were split and later sawn from the

This old ceramic toy is evidence that the Aztecs in medieval Mexico did indeed know the wheel. Grown-ups simply had no use for it.

Left: In one of the chambers of Tutankhamon's grave Carter and his team found a stack of wheels. They weren't mounted to the six chariots, because creep would have deformed them, rather gravely in fact, over a period of over 3000 years.

Right: The remains of Otto Lilïenthal's sailplane 30 years after use.

CREEP

When Tutankhamon's six chariots were found, the archeologists wondered why the wheels weren't mounted to them. Instead they were stacked against the wall. The explanation is simple. A bow long bent at last waxes weak. This holds true for the light flexible laminated chariot wheels too. The rim would bend under the chariot's weight and deform it forever if the wheels weren't removed after use. The other option was to put the vehicle vertically against the wall.
The phenomenon that constructions slowly deform under permanent load is called 'creep'. When engineers calculate structures they assume that elasticity is constant forever and that stress and deformation are proportional. The theoretical consequence is that a structure adapts itself to a certain amount of stress once and for all. In practice, however, most materials behave rather differently. Adaptation is never final.
This is what Gordon adds: 'The amount by which materials creep, however, varies a great deal. Among technological materials, wood, rope and concrete all creep

Super fibres make life easier for structural engineers: no creep.

tree trunk. They were about one metre in diameter. The most common wheel, in use around 3000 BC, consisted of three planks. The one in the middle, the nave, typically was about 20 centimetres thick and in some regions even more. Wheels like this were extremely heavy and so was the carrying construction they supported. The wagons with two or four wheels each were pulled by strong but slow oxen. This made them suitable for moving heavy and bulky loads over short distances, also because nobody bothered to build roads, as boats on rivers took care of the long-distance trade. Wheels could be made slightly lighter by fixing holes in them, but the true innovation came a little earlier than 2000 BC. It was the spoked wheel, with spokes linking the small round nave with an outer rim that could con-

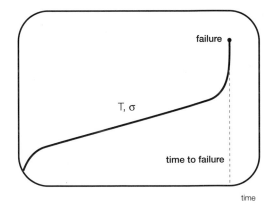

T = applied temperature
σ = applied stress

sist of one piece of bent wood or several segments. This new wheel entailed an entirely different concept of wheeled transport, as two-wheeled wagons were pulled by small horses at a much greater speed.

Around 1800 BC. these chariots became the instrument of power in Mesopotamia and determined the outcome of Eurasian battles for half a millennium. Everywhere rulers tried to employ skilful chariot builders. It didn't take long before these light and fast vehicles were everywhere, from the southeast of China all the way to Sweden. Besides spreading power, charioteers also disseminated the importance of wheeled transport.

At the peak of the era of chariots, their construction had become quite sophisticated. We know from the excavation of Tutankhamon's grave, who died in 1352 BC at the age of 18, that the precision and refinement of chariot technology of that time is unsurpassed, even now. His six wagons – like today royalty was not satisfied with just one means of transportation – was made out of composite materials, like the bow. The Egyptians even succeeded in prestressing the rims, so as to make them less vulnerable to bumps in the ground. Each wheel had six spokes. They were made by bending six wooden strips into a 60 degree V-shape and gluing them together with the points of the V's pointing towards the nave. Furthermore the nave and the central part of the spokes were covered with wet animal skin that shrinks strongly when it dries. This material also served to bind the bent inner and outer parts of the rim together. The builder may have acquired prestress by keeping the two halves of every spoke apart with a peg in the middle when gluing them together. After the assembled spokes had been fitted in the rim he removed the pegs and finished the gluing, pressing the halves together. In this way the spokes were slightly elongated, thus applying tension to the rim, while

very considerably and the effect has to be allowed for. Creep in textiles is one reason why clothes go out of shape and the knees of trousers get baggy; it is, however, much more pronounced in natural fibres, such as wool and cotton, than it is with the newer artificial fibres.

'Creep in metals is generally less pronounced than it is in non-metals, and, although steel creeps significantly at high stresses and when heated, the effect can often be neglected when one is dealing with light loads at ordinary temperatures. 'Creep in any material causes the stress to be redistributed in a manner which is often beneficial, since the more highly stressed parts creep the most. This is why old shoes are more comfortable than new ones. Thus the strength of a

Above: reconstruction drawing of chariot as used in Thebes 1400 BC. Below: Synnik wagon drawing Armenia second millennium BC.

joint may improve with age if the stress concentrations are diminished. Naturally, if the load on the joint is reversed, creep may have the opposite effect and the joint may be weakened.' Slowly giving in to load has caused bridges to fall down and ships to sink. Creep in current wheels is negligible.

Next pages: There is a striking technological resemblance between Tutankhamon's chariot, made out of wood that was imported from the north, and the first wooden chair produced on an industrial scale by Thonet. In both cases wood is bent with the help of heat.

Ask the director of a truck company how much he is prepared to pay for one kilo of weight reduction, he'll say: ten guilders. Nevertheless he doesn't hesitate to buy shiny aluminium wheels, which amount to forty guilders per kilogram...

being onder compression stress themselves.

As it happens, until the beginning of the 1800s all wheels had their spokes under compression whenever they supported the load, each in turn. Gordon says: 'A carriage is therefore rather like a centipede with a great many long legs which, taken together, are heavy and inefficient.' He introduces Sir George Cayley who recognized this problem and invented a solution for light wheels that airplanes could land on safely years before man learned to fly.

Gordon: ' As early as 1808 it occurred to him that a great deal of weight could be saved by designing wheels in which the spokes were in tension rather than compression. This development led, eventually, to the modern bicycle wheel, in which the wire spokes are in tension while compressive forces are taken by the rim, which can be quite light and thin, since it is well stabilized against buckling.'

The load on bicycle wheels is not all that heavy. In cars and trucks and modern aircraft with relatively small wheels, there is not much to be gained from the use of tension spokes, especially because the technology to attach spokes is quite labour-intensive, or time consuming if robots to the work. That is why the disc wheel has made a come-back.

The method of shaping wheels out of sheet metal in the car industry has become quite sophisticated. The other option is moulding them out of light metals, such as aluminium or magnesium. As the quest for lightness is once again gaining importance, so is the attention to different combinations of materials and processes for making lighter wheels. The Dutch company Prins Dokkum bv is developing fibre reinforced polymer trailer wheels that are about 45 percent lighter than aluminium ones, and 64 percent lighter than steel wheels. They have of course all additional advantages of com-

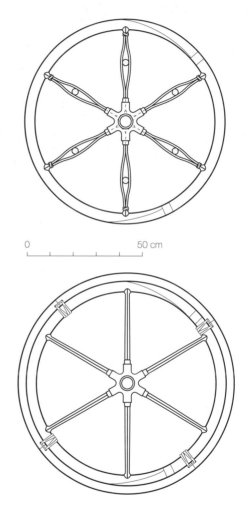

0   50 cm

RESIN TRANSFER MOULDING

Composite wheels can be produced in a process called Resin Transfer Moulding or RTM. First the fibre 'assembly' is placed in a mould that defines the final shape of the product. After that the mould is closed. Then catalysed resin is injected into the mould thus impregnating the textile. After curing the wheel can be removed.

posite: there is no definitive plastic deformation, they can be easily repaired, they need little maintenance and their insulating properties enhance the function of the brakes as the heat generated in the tyres is prevented from reaching them.

In bicycle wheels composite has made its appearance too. Carbon fibre reinforced resin wheels are promising because they combine lightness with relatively easy production and ease of maintenance. A research team in Moscow is even thinking of ways to produce bike wheels in one material, in which properties of elasticity and rubberiness vary within the same structure. If they succeed there will be no separate tyre any longer, just as in the ancient wooden disc wheel. <

The ancient Greeks made wheels with a bronze nave and rim, and wooden spokes. The carbon fibre reinforced RTM wheel is an integral structure. Only the nave is made out of metal.

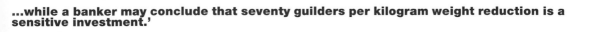

...while a banker may conclude that seventy guilders per kilogram weight reduction is a sensitive investment.'

Trailer gains payload

It took a alliance of no less than 16 participants to develop the 'Cold Feather', a refrigerated trailer that is 30 percent lighter than its predecessors. The past few years there have been earlier modest attempts to reduce trailer weight by just replacing some heavy materials with lighter ones, but in this case the approach resulted in a concept that involved the trinity of form, material and process. The trailer's composite coach is self-supporting and doesn't need the two traditional chassis girders.

The project is a good example of the importance of governmental influence on the development of lighter means of transport. The European standard states that the maximum weight for a loaded trailer truck is 40 metric tons. Since international transport is steadily increasing, it is profitable to reduce the empty truck weight, thereby increasing the potential payload. The only way to drastically reduce the truck mass is to apply composite technology.

Cold Feather is a closed semi-trailer for conditioned (sometimes warmed but more often cooled) transport. It can sustain the freshness of flowers, vegetables, beverages, meat and other perishables like icecream. A conditioned trailer is very suitable for composite redesign, as it must have thick insulating walls anyway. Building a stiff box with cleverly designed sandwich panels can outperform a metal construction in more than one respect and should therefore result in considerable weight reduction.

Generally speaking, steel is very well suited to absorb concentrated peak loads, whereas composites are

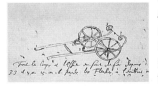

Early 17th century sketch for an iron wagon shows that the invention of iron girders was way before our era.

better in dealing with spreading forces over a large area. They can be tuned to control the amount and the direction of stresses. This principle can clearly be seen in the Cold Feather prototype. The wheel set is lighter than it used to be, with holes in the material, light metal rims and what have you, but the construction that absorbs the forces from the axles is essentially made out of steel. This also holds true for the king pin at the front, the certified link between trailer and truck. However, the trailer lacks the heavy steel beams placed lengthwise under the coach. Their task is completely taken over by the self-supporting box. You also could say that the two beams have been replaced by one that happens to be hollow, and large enough to contain the load. Suddenly the trailer looks strangely empty underneath and this image is made even stronger, because the box in the king pin area is made five centimetres lower. This has been done to avoid level differences in the trailer floor.

This flat floor has a threefold function. It serves as the lower girder. For this reason it should contain fibres that are arranged along the length. Furthermore it must distribute the transverse forces produced by the load to the side panels. To provide the necessary bending stiffness in the transverse direction fibres must therefore also be placed in the 90-degree direction. Last but not least the floor should be able to absorb the forces caused by tilting forklifts and pallet trucks, when the truck is being loaded.

This is why the floor consists of a double panel made up of an upper sandwich and a lower sandwich. The one on top consists of a composite skin reinforced with aramid and a core material of soft and light balsa wood with a high compression strength. The lower skin is made of fibre-glass. In the bottom sandwich the upper skin also consists of fibre-glass, the intermedi-

The Cold Feather steel wheel set is unconventional in that it is made as light as can be managed.

THE ANCIENT TRAILER

Current trailers seem to be a modern invention. They are made out of steel, they have ball bearings around their axles and are fitted with electric lighting and sometimes even a hydraulic lift. Still their construction is basically the same as that of the earliest wagons. Rock carvings in Armenia from the second millennium BC for example show a square structure with two girders under each side of the wagon, to which the axles are attached, and one in the middle that serves as a draught-pole. The only fundamental difference is that in those days wagons were pulled by oxen, whereas nowadays a motorized truck does all the heavy work.

'Truck companies appear to find it difficult to accept the quality of lightness.'

ate layer is made out of PVC foam and the lower skin out of aluminium sheet. The floor's protective layer for friction wear is thinner than usual, since the aramid skin is highly resistant to wear.

The coach looks simple enough, but appearances are deceptive. The forces that used to be absorbed by the chassis girders of earlier versions, now have to find their way to the side panels. For this purpose eight carbon reinforced resin beams have been integrated in the floor and the sides at strategically chosen locations. At the back four have been bolted to the wheel set. Two ribs are linked to the king pin at the front and for extra stiffness there are two in the middle. Their blackness can be seen gleaming through the aramid-epoxy skin before the coach has received its coating. In everyday practice more ribs may be necessary, depending on the sort of load that the trailer has to contain. Meat, for instance, must be hung from bars that are attached to the walls, which would need extra reinforcement.

Corners in sandwich panels can be made in several different ways. Milling a V-shaped groove and consequent folding doesn't provide strong ones, neither does direct shaping by hand lay-up. In this case specially designed extruded aluminium profiles have been glued in the corners in such a way that they interweave the sandwich panel rims with each other. The corner radius at the front amounts no less than 160 millimetres, to decrease air resistance. The roundings are filled with poly-urethane foam.

Laminating the panels was a specialist job in building the prototype. No doubt experience and scaling up the process will make things easier and cheaper. After all, the materials were unusual for the involved parties. The foam in the panels is PVC, because it is stronger and has better compression resistance than poly-

'In a traditional context new concepts sometimes only make it through risk sharing by consensus, otherwise you get a guerrilla against renewal.'

Aerodynamic shaping may reduce fuel consumption by some 2000 litres per year in long distance truck transport.

styrene or poly-urethane. Moreover its durability is outstanding. Because of the absence of corrosion and weakening by fatigue the new trailer is bound to last longer than conventional ones.

The aramid textile in the panels consists of a layer of perpendicular fibres and an other identical layer placed under 45 degrees with its weaving direction. In this way the panels are able to absorb loads in all directions. The supplier is considering marketing this combination of textiles as a complete product. This would simplify sandwich production. The choice fell on aramid mainly because of its lightness. Moreover these fibres are better resistant to impact than glass or carbon, which reduces the chance of damage. For that matter the coach can be repaired in the usual way, by applying a new patch of textile and fixing it with resin. The Cold Feather, for which the Faculty of Aerospace Engineering of the University of Technology in Delft delivered the basic concepts, is 3000 kilograms lighter than traditional cooling trailers. Because of its lightness it consumes less fuel per unit load, or transports more goods. It is therefore cheaper to run and the higher investment can be recovered in an estimated two and a half years.

The trailer is the first of its kind. The advantage of composite materials is that trailers for different purposes can be made in different shapes. <

CHEAP TRUCKING
For trucks the costs of fuel consumption, that are related directly to truck weight, are just as important as the total investments costs. The average weight saving – the extra load capacity cannot always be exploited to the maximum – is 2250 kilograms. If the extra investment for a lighter truck is estimated at 30,000 guilders and the economic life span is 11 years, then the return on the extra investment takes less than four years. The extra net profit amounts to NLG 6000,- per trailer per year.

light-weight economics

Wim Hafkamp

Constructions in the perspective of a sustainable economy

Lightness is not a word that appears in the economic literature. If it means anything at all to economists, they will associate lightness with heads, or fingers, but not with the weight of materials, components or structures. This is hardly surprising, considering that economics, after all's said and done, is not so much concerned with investigating processes of physics, but processes of choice. Choice processes as a rule do not have physical dimensions. However, it is possible for their results to have a physical dimension: for example, the success of a steel plant is often measured in tons of product. A haulage company is doing well if its ton-kilometres are rising. The port of Rotterdam breaks the sound barrier when throughput exceeds 300 million tons. If weight plays any part in economic thinking, then it is a matter of 'the more the merrier'. Heaviness is a measure of success.

Incidentally, the word lightness is even absent from the dictionary of the environmental economist. This is actually rather strange. Environmental economics, after all, is precisely concerned with investigating the physical implications of economic processes and the problems that arise as a result of them: pollution, depletion of natural resources, and so on. In the seventies the US environmental economist Herman Daly used the metaphor of the ship (the economy) that was lying too deep in the water (the physical environment). Heaviness as a problem. Lightness as a challenge.

This 'metaphorical' challenge was to trigger a large number of developments in the areas of policy, technology and organization, both in companies and in governments. Here I wish to highlight one of these and then go on to examine the incredible importance of light structures and materials. I will refer to the consultation document on the environment and the economy published by the Dutch government in the past year. I take this particular document because it is a very recent piece of work which enjoys wide support in industry, politics and environmental organizations, and above all because it takes this 'metaphorical' lightness as a central challenge.

In this note 'Environment and Economy' Dutch government outlines a 'perspective' of sustainable economic development in the following terms:
In sustainable economic development people's needs are the central issue. The means of meeting those needs are changing fast. The needs of consumers are being met with tailor-made solutions with a strong emphasis on quality and service. It is a matter of qualitatively high-value products (long useful life, extensive in terms of materials and energy), but also of sustainable

building and living, and new transport systems. Developing nature and com-
bining functions in rural areas contribute to the preservation of biodiversity
and people's need for clean air, quiet, and a varied natural environment.
There are new services (e.g. media, infotainment/entertainment, electronic
services), old services (e.g. education, care, culture) and product/service
combinations (shared cars). In this way it is possible to offer a competitive
response to the specific high-value wishes of customers in markets both old
and new.

In the perspective of sustainable economic development the economy
grows at the same rate as the physical burden on resources and energy and
the production of waste and emissions falls. Material and resource flows
move through the economy in cascades and cycles, so there is no accumula-
tion of pollution. The greatest possible use is made of renewable resources
and sustainable energy. Often the environment itself is used multifunctionally
as a production factor (for transport, for its ability to purify water and soil, for
agricultural produce, for recreation, for water extraction, for its nature value,
for energy, and for spatial quality). Space is used multifunctionally and effi-
ciently, while its quality remains intact.

The first and most important element of sustainable economic development is that meeting the needs of people is at the forefront: housing, food,
transport, clothing, recreation, and so on. Our present ways of meeting these
needs are relatively burdensome on the environment, so the answer lies not
primarily in less housing or less food, but in finding innovative, environmentally sparing ways of meeting them. Innovations, whether incremental or by
breakthroughs, can be achieved in the fields of technology, management and
organization, institutions, and combinations of these.

In this context the use of light materials in ultra light structures is of crucial importance. It often allows superior function-fulfilment at the cost of a
significantly lower overall environmental impact. There are examples in transport, such as aircraft and refrigerated vans, and industrial activities such as
packaging and construction, that demonstrate this. This brings us to a second element: quality. Lightweight structures often accommodate high-quality
function-fulfilment because they are stiffer, offer better temperature and noise
insulation, and deliver more net usable floor area.

The third element, dematerialization, is encapsulated within the other two.
Here it is a matter of 'doing more (function fulfilment) with less (physical

material)', or in the terminology of Daly: the added value rises, while that to which value is added decreases. This is a process often termed the shifting of the economy towards services. Here I draw a distinction between services-in-the-product (design, communication, function fulfilment), services-pertaining-to-the-product (product/service combinations) and services-without-products (business/personal services). Light structures are a perfect example of the first category, services-in-the-product: both in the design and the production of new high-value materials and in the design of the structure itself. Lots of added value to not many kilos.

A fourth element in sustainable economic development is the way in which materials and resources move through our economy. No longer is it a one-way process. It runs in cycles and long cascades. Lightweight materials, particularly composites, and the structures based on them, often find themselves in 'environmental difficulties' because they cannot be recycled or re-used. This is a serious drawback which ought at the very least to give the designers of materials and structures pause for thought – and if at all possible, not just defensive thought. Both the materials used in composites and the technology of gluing and bonding still need to be improved to the point at which recycling and reuse can be 'built in' at a very early stage in the lifecycle of materials and products.

At the same time this technology also holds a promise, because it accommodates drastic reductions in fuel consumption in existing processes. This in turn brings within view the use of renewable energy in processes in which this has hitherto not been possible, as in transport or refrigeration and heating. As substitution of this kind becomes possible on a larger scale, so too there will be more opportunities for meeting what remains of the demand for fossil fuels. They include secondary fuels derived from synthetic materials from the petrochemicals industry, and perhaps also from biomass, both of which will already have past lives behind them in a succession of other products.

Instead of very rapidly turning oil into petrol, diesel or heating fuel, and then immediately burning these to produce traction or heating, we shall use the same crude oil first as synthetics and plastics in materials, products and structures, until, after a very long cascade, we will finally use them as fuel. In this way the average dwell time for oil in the economic system can rise from a few weeks to many decades, perhaps even centuries. Now this may be far ahead in the future, and it is only possible in combination with large-scale use of renewable energy. However, in any event, ultra light structures are certain to play a crucial role.

In short, looking at it from the angle of sustainable economic development, lightweight materials and structures are of incredibly great importance. In the foregoing I have looked at the direct effects, the immediate importance of lightness. There are also indirect effects. If structures and products are light, and use significantly less energy and allow greater useful performance (consider the recent use of lightweight constructions in refrigerated transport), then this also means that there is a reduction in the burden, or at least in the growth of the burden, on the infrastructure – not just roads, but the energy and water infrastructure too. In the light of the heated social and political arguments about expanding the infrastructure of roads, airports and seaports in the Netherlands, these indirect effects are also important. The cost of expanding the conventional infrastructure must be compared with the cost of increasing the efficiency of logistics, distribution and passenger traffic.

So is everything hunky-dory with the development of ultra-lightweight structures? At first sight it looks like it, but some reservations remain. We can use technological progress like this to increase the environmental performance, or eco-efficiency, of products, but we can also use it to satisfy other, latent or new, needs: safety, speed, comfort, etcetera. We can see this in long-life light bulbs (high light output and low overall cost, leading to new, more careless applications and use so that on balance our consumption of fuel for lighting still goes up) and in cars (more economical engines and new construction methods and materials translating into safer, heavier cars with higher net fuel consumption). This is the so-called rebound effect.

Innovations and breakthrough technologies are a necessary but not a sufficient condition for the achievement of a sustainable economy. Consumer preferences, and the way consumers allow new ecological values to play a part in their behaviour and purchasing decisions, are at least as important, as are the relative prices of the goods and services on which they spend their household budgets.

Bridging
the gap

From early on man has adapted the landscape in which he lives to accommodate his mobility. In steep mountainous regions, where the use of wagons and domesticated animals was unknown, people crossed rivers and narrow chasms by dangerously making their way across fallen trees, or tree trunks laid down for the occasion. If a gorge happened to be too deep and wide for this he built simple but dangerous suspension bridges out of rope. Here pure tension has always controlled bridge construction.

Rivers, however, also flow slowly through flat lands where wheeled transport has existed for thousands of years. As long as the need to cross the water was incidental, wading would suffice and the occasional wet leg was taken for granted. Where the vastness of the

The beaver dam concept is obtrusive to the landscape. A primitive suspension bridge presents a more elegant solution.

This old Celtic bridge in Scotland demonstrates the carrying capacity of a worn down arch.

stream didn't allow crossing, ferries were used. With the increase of traffic the building of bridges became inevitable. You might say that this growth has manifested itself through a gradual but fundamental change in the character of nomadism. Whereas small groups of people used to migrate on and on, from one settlement to another, now millions generally live in closely packed urban areas and move back and forth frequently, to commute or to go shopping or to take the

'Structurally a suspension bridge is like a spider's web, functionally it is exactly the opposite.'

The better weight is distributed along a cable or a thread the more these take the shape of perfect catenaries.

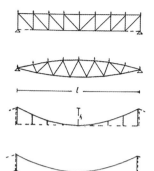

The diagrams from top to bottom show the increase of structural efficiency in bridge development.

kids to school. The ability to do this depends on the presence of tunnels and bridges. Interestingly the explosive transport growth of the past century has called for ever lighter bridges over ever wider gaps. This tendency reveals itself in tension gradually taking over from compression in bridge structures.

The first bridges were made out of wood. Julius Caesar had a 400 metre long wooden construction made across the river Rhine. Bridges that big don't last if they're made of wood. Stone ones do. When labour is cheap masonry is the obvious technology for building bridges, arch bridges to be exact. They have been around since early Roman times and their quality is proven by the fact that some bridges and aqueducts have survived two millennia. Some of them even have been in use until this very day.

According to Gordon in his book 'Structures', an arch bridge can span more than 60 metres, providing the height of the arch amounts to at least half that figure. If the spanned ravine is deep enough this should pose no problem, as there will be little or no elevation in the road. Lack of depth, however, forces builders to make sloping approaches, or the bridge would be too steep to climb for vehicles, trains in particular.

Several alternatives appeared in due time. The first was the cast iron bridge. Apart from the advantage that arches could be made flatter, the prefabricated parts were cheaper than extensive masonry. Moreover casting of iron allowed for openings in the construction that made it drastically lighter, thereby keeping down the costs of transportation of bridge building materials and allowing for more modest abutments. Still, like stone, cast iron is a brittle material that is very good in distributing compression stresses, but unreliable in dealing with tension. British railroad companies suffered severe losses in the mid-1800s when a vast number of

Next pages: The bridge club is testing the structure for the famous bridge across the Firth of Forth. Two persons take part as structural members. The man in the middle is supposed to be the load.

120

'Bridges always show how they are put together.'

MAXIMUM SPAN

To speed up traffic between Europe and Africa a fixed link between the two continents is under consideration. One option is a tunnel, the other a bridge across the Strait of Gibraltar. A conventional steel suspension bridge would only be able to span the distance of no less than 22 kilometres if it were divided into ten equal portions of two kilometres each and two end sections of one kilometre. Apart from such a bridge being about twice as expensive as a tunnel, it would also hinder sea traffic.

In 1987 the Swiss bridge specialist Meier calculat-ed an alternative carbon cable-stayed bridge of the fan type. The deck was to be suspended from two towers with heights of 850 and 1250 metres respectively, perhaps hampering air traffic instead of ships. Carbon fibre cables allow a span of 8400 metres.

Meier proposed a very simple way of calculating the maximum span of bridges. It is character-ized by the use of the ratio (y) between cable weight and payload, the latter being the total of the bridge deck and all trucks, cars and trains on it. In the graphs we use y = 0.5 as a starting point. Its importance: recently the steel deck of several

identical bridges in France was replaced by an aluminium version to increase its capacity to carry traffic.

Furthermore a safety factor is involved, just in case. It is used to reduce

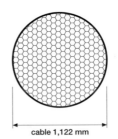

cable 1,122 mm

cast iron beam bridges – no arches, just beams – were built. Robert Stephenson, the well-known inventor of the first 'Rocket' steam locomotive, designed them, but not very cleverly. They appeared unable to withstand the bending forces that inevitably occurred when a train passed and had to be demolished.

A more traditional option was to be pigheaded and build a daringly flat brick arch bridge, like the famous bridge designer Brunel did across the Thames in 1837. It had two arches, each with a span of 38 metres and a rise of just 7 metres. Gordon: 'Both the public and the experts were horrified, and the papers were full of letters prophesying that the bridge would never stand. To keep the correspondence and the publicity going, and

The main cables used in suspension bridges should not be intertwined, but parallel, so that they can move slightly alongside each other. This excludes the occurrence of bending stiffness.

pre-tension cable properties

	σ (10⁶ N/m²)	ρ (10³ kgf/m³)	E (10⁹ N/m²)
steel	1860	7.9	200
glass fibre	1700	2.1	50
carbon fibre	2400	1.7	140
aramid fibre	2000	1.5	70

fibre properties specified for UD-pultrusions with 60% fibre volume

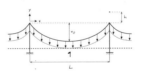

$$S \leq \left\{ \frac{\lambda}{\beta\left(1+\frac{1}{y}\right)} \right\} \cdot \left\{ \frac{\bar{\sigma}}{\rho \cdot g} \right\}$$

main span s

Each and every year the Golden Gate bridge needs 17,000 litres of red lead for maintenance.

perhaps to gratify his sense of humour, Brunel delayed removing the wooden centering or false-work on which the arches had been erected. Naturally, it was said that he was frightened to do so. When, after about a year, the centering was destroyed in a storm, the arches stood perfectly well. Brunel then revealed that the centering had, in fact, been eased to a clearance of a few inches soon after the brickwork was in place and had been doing nothing at all for many months. The bridge is still there today, carrying trains about ten times as heavy as Brunel ever intended.' Eiffel did things likewise. The arch frames among the feet of his tower mainly serve to make the construction look trustworthy. They don't contribute to the basic structure.

In the beginning of the 20th century the supremacy of compression started to wear off. It started with the construction of bridges with two parallel concrete or

the risk of failure at maximum load and to increase the wisdom of technicians. In aeronautical engineering a safety factor of 1.5 is usual. This simply means that, if calculations show that the thickness of a certain part must be 10 millimetres, you'd better make it 15 millimetres, just in case. Of course material is represented in the formulas too, by its density,

its strength (or the tension stress in maximum elastic deformation) and its stiffness, expressed in Young's modulus.

There is one last parameter that defines the distinction in cable stress between the suspension bridge and the cable stayed bridge.

The specific design load can be plotted against the span. Among other things the graphs show that suspension bridges generally perform much better than stayed ones and that carbon is far more efficient than steel in building bridges. It also

'Bridges have a natural beauty. Building a bridge is always a positive action.'

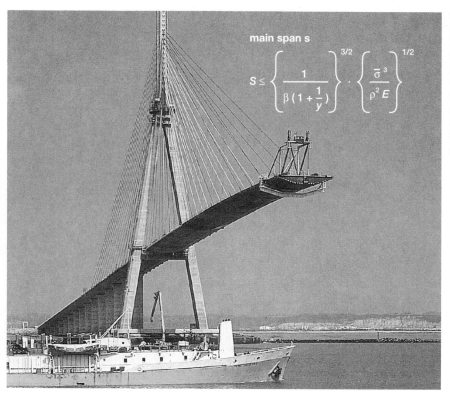

main span s

$$S \leq \left\{ \frac{1}{\beta \left(1 + \frac{1}{y}\right)} \right\}^{3/2} \cdot \left\{ \frac{\bar{\sigma}^3}{\rho^2 E} \right\}^{1/2}$$

shows that if the ratio between cables and payload is 0.5, building a steel bridge across the Strait of Messina with a combined safety factor for cables and the entire system of 5.36 is tricky to say the least. The safe thing to do would be to allow no traffic on it.

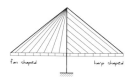

fan shaped   harp shaped

steel arches. The deck is not guided over them, but suspended in between, thus definitively solving the problem of the approaches being too steep. The first one was Hell Gate bridge, built in New York in 1915. It spanned 300 metres. Even more awesome was the Sidney Harbour bridge with a length of 500 metres. This type of bridge is still popular and subject to aesthetic experiments. In 1995 Arenas and Pantaleon designed a bridge for Expo '92 in Seville, with a single arch in the middle that spreads out in Y-shaped forks at both ends. In this way the road is not 'clamped' in between two

INSTRUCTIVE TRAGEDIES

Twenty De Havilland DH 106 Comets have crashed, killing a total of 480 people. It was the first jet propelled airliner. Two major crashes, caused by explosions at high altitude, were due to structural faults that nobody can be blamed for. It took an enormous research

effort to be able to conclude that the accidents were due to a combination of aluminium fatigue and stress concentrations at rivet holes around cutouts in the pressurized fuselage. Up until the crashes the importance of these phenomena was not recognized. Not a soul was aware of the complicated conditions

suspension bridge versus cable stayed bridge

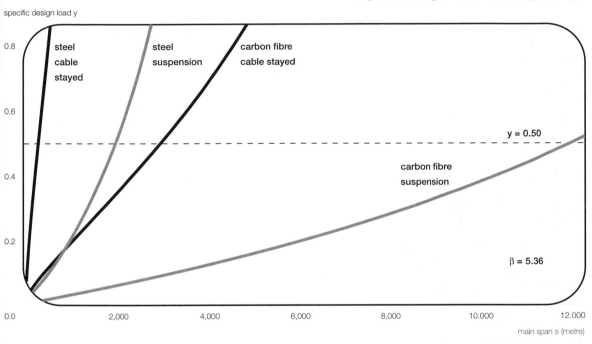

specific design load y

0.8 — steel cable stayed | steel suspension | carbon fibre cable stayed

0.6

y = 0.50

0.4 — carbon fibre suspension

0.2

β = 5.36

0.0 | 2,000 | 4,000 | 6,000 | 8,000 | 10.000 | 12.000

main span s (metre)

maximum span s (metre); β = 5.36

specific design load	steel stayed	steel suspension	carbon fibre stayed	carbon fibre suspension
y = 0.25	160	1,190	1,330	7,120
y = 0.33	230	1,470	1,840	8,830
y = 0.50	**350**	**1,980**	**2,870**	**11,860**
⋮	⋮	⋮	⋮	⋮
y = inf.	1,830	5,990	14,890	35,580

$$Y = \frac{W_{cable}}{W_{deck} + W_{traffic}} \qquad W = weight$$

Brooklyn Bridge in New York has a
structure that combines the principles
of the suspension bridge and the
cable-stayed bridge.

that jet airliners must be able to withstand. Nevertheless the daring and costly development of the Comet can be considered an important contribution to today's aviation.

Other major disasters concern bridges, mostly during construction. A few of the most tragic failures during erection were the collapse of the cantilever, due to buckling of the main chords, and a little later the suspended span of the Quebec bridge in 1907 causing 87 deaths. Aerodynamic oscillations spectacularly brought down the Tacoma Narrows bridge in the US in 1940. Today much effort is being devoted to ensuring the safety of bridges during erection. The new Akashi Kaikyo suspension bridge in Japan has survived two earthquakes during its construction.

No matter how hard we try to prevent them, accidents will always happen. They are the experiments and tests designers did not think of, either because nobody could have possibly foreseen what would happen, or because they were blind

to previous experience. Tragic though accidents may be, they are always instructive.

arches but rather hangs underneath just one.

The next thing to do is turn Antoni Gaudí upside down, his way of determining building structure that is. The architect used string under tension to define the shape of arches. A suspension bridge evolves from thinking in the opposite direction. The difference is that a brick semi-circular arch turns into a catenary when gravity shapes it. Hanging a straight piece of road from a catenary represents a rather drastic change in design approach, particularly for people not living in steep mountainous areas.

The steel cable suspension bridge – essentially still a two-dimensional structure – has become enormously popular in the 20th century, but the principle was first exploited some 250 years ago, when steel had yet to be discovered. The deck was suspended from a wrought-iron chain, not unlike the kind that is used in bicycles, only bigger. As the chains became cheaper the suspension bridge grew to be a practical solution for guiding wheeled vehicles over rivers. Brunel reached the maximum span for this type of bridge in the Clifton bridge with 190 metres. The main drawback for larger spans is the weight of the chains themselves,

increasing cable tensile strength

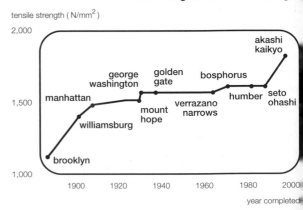

tensile strength (N/mm^2)

increasing length of centre span

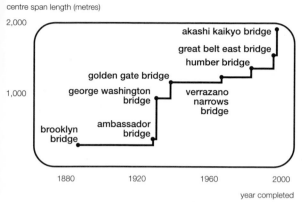

centre span length (metres)

2,000

akashi kaikyo bridge

great belt east bridge

humber bridge

golden gate bridge

george washington
bridge

verrazano
narrows
bridge

1,000

brooklyn
bridge

ambassador
bridge

1880   1920   1960   2000

year completed

across the Strait of Messina is projected between Sicily and Italy's mainland. The required span between the main towers is 3.3 kilometres and it is not sure whether a construction like that will collapse because of its own weight.

The alternative is of course to make cables out of carbon fibre reinforced polymers, thus doubling or even tripling the maximum span of steel suspension bridges. As it happens several small composite bridges have already been built. They're promising because of their superior structural efficiency, and also because they don't tend to become rusty over the years. <

See 'in depth' for more information.

or rather the material efficiency of wrought-iron. The invention of steel brought about a gigantic improvement. Steel cables of a thickness in the region of sometimes over a metre that consist of parallel thinner cables to avoid the danger of bending stresses, allow bridges to be built with a span eight times as long as the Clifton chain bridge. The latest one is built in Japan, between Kobe and the island of Awaji, as part of an ambitious road network. The span of the central section is almost two kilometres. The towers reach up to 283 metres above sea level.

This century a different kind of cable bridge saw the light. Here the roadway is not suspended from one or two thick catenaries to which it is attached by thin cables. Instead it is stayed by cables directly to a central tower. There are two principles involved. Either the cables are all guided over the tower top (the fan-system), or they follow a parallel route through the pylon at different heights (harp-system). The former is slightly better because the angle at which the cables closest to the tower rises assures more efficient guiding of stresses. Plans for new bridges get ever more ambitious, in fact so ambitious that the material efficiency of steel cables comes into question. For instance a suspension bridge

In several of these (bicycle chain) bridges in France the steel deck was replaced by an aluminium one to increase the payload.

Frozen fabrics

'A great deal of money is spent on economic feasibility studies, but technical feasibility is taken for granted.'

Fashion designers know extremely well how to drape fabrics. The fibre textiles that reinforce polymers show similar behaviour.

The longer fibres are, the more you can do with them. Even spiders and caterpillars seem to realize this. They succeed in weaving a single thread into respectively trap-nets and bedclothes that are crucial to their lifestyles. Until 20 or 30 years ago threads used by humans always consisted of short naturally grown protein based fibres that had to be spun or otherwise intertwined. The distaff, a small spinning wheel on a vertical axle existed way before the invention of wheeled transport. Nowadays endless synthetic filaments are made in a continuous production process. High quality composites can be made on the basis of fabrics wrought out of these strong continuous fibres.

In general fabrics can be considered the two-dimensional counterpart of strings and cables. Whereas both basic structuring materials exclusively absorb tension stress, fabrics are able to do this in more directions. To distribute forces they have an entire surface at their disposal instead of just a line. Therefore they are ideal for creating light objects. They can be stretched into tents or formed into airplanes as a component of composites. Essentially stiff composite parts consist of some kind of textile material that is frozen into its shape by a polymer matrix. This can be thermosetting, in which case the fabric is usually draped in the right shape before impregnation. Winding around a specially formed coil or braiding serves to make hollow structures. For open shell structures one uses the classic hand lay-up method. It involves laying the fibrous material in a

SIMULATED DRAPING
Machine draping of composites is by no means as easy as it seems. That is what your findings will be if you try to develop a computer program to simulate the process. Not

only fabric and polymer characteristics determine what will happen, but so do the effect of clamping, friction between material and mould and temperature changes as the result of contact between them. The only way to develop this kind of software is to make simplifying assumptions and check their practicality. Already in 1956 a study was done on covering a continuous revolution surface with fabric. The main conclusion was that, geometrically, fabric behaves like a fisherman's net and that shearing takes care of the largest portion of deformation. For simulation purposes fabric can be considered a network of warp and weft fibres that can hinge around the intersecting contact

From left to right these drawings show the principles of braiding, weaving and knitting, all of which can be applied to composite materials.

mould and then applying resin to it, with a brush, a roller or a spray gun. A slightly more advanced technology is resin transfer moulding, whereby the resin is injected in the mould under pressure. The advantage of both these methods is that fibre orientation in different layers can be controlled with some accuracy. However, they bear the risk of creating an unhealthy breathing environment and are labour intensive. Machines find it difficult to manipulate cloth because of its unpredictable behaviour. The latter factor is the most important reason why it has so far been difficult for composites to compete with metal. Although advanced continuous fibre reinforced composites may perform well from a structural point of view, future success depends on the availability of fast and accurate manufacturing processes.

A cleaner and cheaper way of handling fibre reinforced polymers is to take care of the impregnation in advance, preferably with a thermoplastic polymer, in an industrial automated process. In this way you get 'prepregs': sheet material that can be shaped by heating and bending. Several layers can be stuck or welded together. According to this principle some airplane parts are already made out of unidirectional thermoset tapes. They consist of an impregnated band of parallel fibres. Since this production method involves cutting pieces of tape to the right size, arranging them and fixing them in the right place, it is not unlike making a

Draping of a welder's shield was simulated on a computer to optimize the shape.

points between them. Neglecting the other modes of deformation, such as stretching, appears to provide more plausible predictions. As a matter of fact shearing deformation predicted by the computer is always greater than in reality. All is well as long as reality is milder than theory. Most geometrical simulation approaches proceed from a chosen location of the first warp and weft yarn, from which deformation of the rest of the fabric is derived. The disadvantage is that fabric can be draped in or around a mould in an endless number of ways.

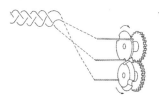

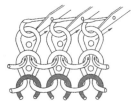

Moreover the fabric may already be deformed before draping. An alternative is to avoid this initial guesswork by choosing a strategy depending on the shape to be produced. An example is the highest point strategy for rotational symmetric shapes. It starts from the highest point of the fabric's edge and calculates deformation from there.

A different computational approach is the finite element method. Generally speaking a structure is divided in small parts, in which deformation parameters are calculated. A thin walled structure made out of woven fabric with a polymer matrix can, for calculating purposes, be divided into numerous little interlocking rectangular or triangular membranes. However, they are not very well suited for the deformation of fabric, because of the relatively large shear deformation. A better choice is to define the fabric as a collection of truss elements. The finite elements method is able to make more accurate predictions. On the other hand the software is still slow

and there are problems with interfacing and establishing failure criterions. Improvements are presently being worked on.

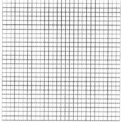

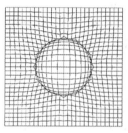

Draping of geometric shapes shows the step by step approach of computer simulation, to predict what will happen. (Left: draping)

photo collage and still quite labour intensive.

Very promising, from the automation point of view, is forming pre impregnated woven or knitted fabrics. Mankind has come a long way in mastering them. Fabrics provide us with clothing, a lightweight flexible personal microclimate that even allows migration from the hot desert to the cool mountains if necessary. The textile industry is one of the oldest, largest and most flexible in existence. Draping and shaping textiles into dresses, jackets, trousers, hats and shoes, according to ever faster changing fashions for ever more demanding individuals, is now commonplace.

Of course forming composites is not exactly the same

'Pleats are usually avoided, but they may contribute to the structural quality.'

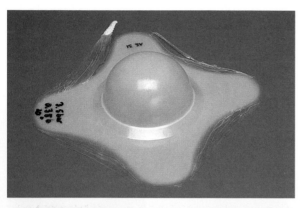

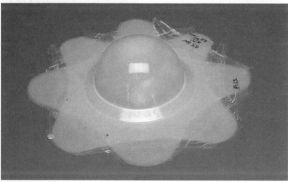

FLYING CIGARS

Unlike a Cuban cigar, that has entire rolled-up tobacco leaves inside, typically the Dutch cigar consists of a mixture of cut tobacco in a binder, which in its turn is rolled into a wrapper. The expensive and vulnerable wrapper determines an important part of the aroma and is supposed to make the cigar airtight. Designing a new cigar model for mass production takes quite some time, because a new shape involves a new contour that has to be cut out of the tobacco leaf in such a way that it will fit nicely around the cigar before it is glued in place at the mouthpiece. A solution to speed up the design process was required.

Some knowledge about fibre winding was available at the Faculty for Aerospace Engineering. The people there got very interested in the idea of winding band material as thread has the disadvantage that it piles up at places where the coil diameter is smaller. Eric Otten graduated at the Faculty of Mechanical Engineering and Marine Technology with an extension to the thread winding software that helps to wind the band. His idea used two parallel

thing as draping silk, wool or synthetic materials, but draping clothes sets a wonderful example. This is an idea that takes some getting used to for specialist designers in the car, train, shipping, airplane or building industry, since they tend to think in sound, heavy and stiff materials that you can lean against, and not in the flexible stuff that fashion designers like Vivienne Westwood or Issey Miyake appear to have complete control of.
The Structures and Materials Laboratory of the Faculty of Aerospace Engineering in Delft has discovered the

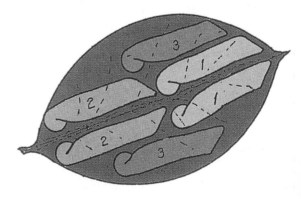

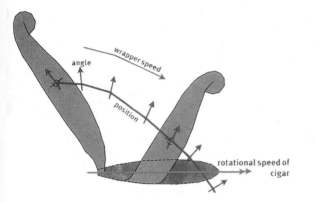

angle
wrapper speed
position
rotational speed of cigar

threads instead of one, to represent the piece of tobacco wrapper. The software can determine the optimal leaf contour for a certain cigar shape. As the leaf can withstand deformation, winding it can be considered a form of draping. In principle Otten's software could be the starting point to develop a fibre reinforced polymer airplane fuselage. The only difference with a cigar is that composites are less vulnerable and that the glue must be applied to the nose of the airplane instead of its tail for aerodynamic reasons, assuming of course that a cigar is lit at the front. The general idea is to avoid air resistance of overlapping coiled composite layers.

potential of draping prepregs. Research is currently being done on ways to control it on an industrial scale. More and more is being found out about the behaviour of different kinds of fabric. Computer programs are being developed for draping simulation.

Draping a thermoplastic composites sheet is done in a press, after it has been made deformable by heating. It is a matter of seconds, and afterwards consolidation takes place in matching dies. The speed is comparable with that of injection moulding. The equipment needed is relatively simple and light. Since the applied pressures are not extremely high the dies are inexpensive. A combination of several effects on fibres and their interaction determines what happens to a fabric when it is deformed while under tension. Individual threads are either straightened if they are interwoven with other ones or they are stretched. The opposite of stretching, buckling, can happen as well, but should be avoided as it implies weakening of the product. Deformation can also imply bending.

In combination, threads can shear – known as the trellis effect – which means that for example a square in between four threads deforms into a diamond shape.

WOVEN HELMET

The item of clothing that has to meet the highest demands is without doubt the military helmet. Up until a few years ago they were made out of steel. This may sound surprising but the more a product determines individual physical safety, the more careful one is in following new technological trends.

The helmet evolves from a compromise between the protection it is supposed to provide against shrapnel flying around, and wearing comfort. It must function in extreme cold and extreme heat alike. Moreover its properties should be able to withstand daily use, which among soldiers is not always careful.

During the test period for

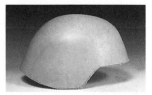

'The only disadvantage of a composite helmet is that you can't cook in one.'

instance, someone hung his helmet on the exhaust pipe of a truck.
It is clear that fibre reinforced plastics are unequalled for protection against impact. For additional reasons of weight and heat resistance the new helmet is made out of about twenty layers of aramid fibre reinforced resin. It weighs about 200 grams less than its metal predecessor.

Face protection shield and welder's shield made out of composite materials are safe and light.

Shearing dominates in deformation. A less desirable effect is an increase in the distance between parallel threads, called shear slip. One can observe all these phenomena in a stretched handkerchief that is pushed against the head of a large nail.

Formability of composites appears to predominantly depend on the fibre pattern. Fibres can be woven in numerous different ways, depending on the number of warp threads going over and under the weft threads and the alternation herein. Research has shown that the polymer increases formability because of some kind of lubricating effect. Deformation is easiest in a so called satin weave with small yarn bundles and a large yarn spacing.

There is one more deformation effect. Laminates consist of at least two woven layers, with polymer layers in between. In a thermo-forming process, such as rubber forming (between one steel hollow mould and one protruding rubber mould), the polymer layers, softened by heat, will allow the woven layers to move along each other. This is called interply slipping. Obviously optimization of deforming properties leads to a decrease in strength and stiffness. As ever, material, process and shape need fine tuning for every application.

Up until know we have mainly discussed relatively flat fibre structures. Three-dimensional weaving is another option. It just might be possible for example to make hollow composite sheets, that can be filled with foam or used to contain fluids or gases. Moreover we only have to look at a complicated Irish sweater to realize that we have hardly begun to explore the possibilities of shaping thermoplastic composites. Knitting opens up a whole new area of composite deformation properties. <

Flimsy buildings

Left: an image of settling or maybe
even the first steps towards the origi-
nation of a city. When you walk
through this village the first structures
you encounter are hardly more than
simple tents covered with mud and
straw. The further you go the more
definite the buildings are. The last
ones are true stone houses.

The collection of tents at the average holiday camp is
but a faint reflection of the world of portable dwellings.
There is such a richness of variation in constructions
details and use of light buildings that we can only lift a
corner of the canvas. Some tents travel over enormous
distances and some are just moved a couple of metres
to avoid the necessity of cleaning the floor. One kind of
tents functions best in a particular climate, while
another can be adapted to many sorts of extreme
weather conditions. Differences also depend on the
availability of materials: why pack the framework and
take it with you in the morning when you know you'll
be able to gather fresh wood for a new one at the end
of a day's travel.

Basically there are two principles for tent structures. In
one the prevailing process is spanning cloth with tension wires over poles and in the other mats are draped
around a more elaborate wooden framework that can
stand on its own. The tension structures are lighter
and mainly used by nomads. Draped tents, inhabited
by shepherd tribes, tend to be kept in the same place
for a longer period of time. More often than tensile
tents, they may be in use as sedentary dwellings. As
for any rule there are exceptions. Draped tents were
sometimes built on wheels. Remember the one
Genghis Kahn travelled in.

The 'black tent' is the most widespread stretched tent.

'The chances of combining functions with the help of material properties are too often ignored.'

It is the dwelling of the tribes that wander across the arid areas of North Africa and the Middle East all the way to the eastern border of Tibet. In fact 'Arab' literally translates into 'tent dweller'. According to Torvald Faegre in his book on nomadic architecture, the birthplace of the black tent is probably Mesopotamia and it must have originated at the time of the domestication of sheep and goats that gratefully gave up their hair to spin and weave the fabric to build them. Goat hair provides the basic material. Sometimes hair of sheep and camels and plant fibres are added. In the eastern regions hair of yaks prevails over goat hair.

This type of shelter obviously owes its name to the colour of the cloth it is made out of. Those who are interested in physics may find it difficult to believe that tents used in the desert are black, since this colour is supposed to absorb heat and therefore expected to make a dwelling extremely uncomfortable in hot arid conditions. At closer examination the dark cloth is a fine example of combining functions in a light and

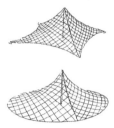

Peaked black tents in the Sahara desert. Inside them it can be as much as 30 degrees Celsius cooler than outside.

FLYING TENTS
Ambiguity is the main characteristic of kites. The most common thing to do is regard the kite as an old toy-like predecessor of the airplane. After all kites have been around for 3000 years. On the other hand they exist in such an enormous variety that many of them can be considered architecture as well.
Bernard Rudofsky in his book 'The prodigious builders' certainly does so: 'Surely giant kites have a claim to be con-

Architects are fascinated by the lightness and the functionality of tent structures. The most advanced interpretations use textile. With just cables, as in the Munich stadium, the result is exciting because of its vastness.

sidered architectural borderline cases. A 4-ton kite is not a toy, nor could flying it be called child's play. Yet if it is not a toy, neither is it a vehicle; one cannot travel by kite. By stretching a point, one might call it shelter, since occasionally it did accommodate a person. Aerial spotting was practiced long before the advent of flying machines, and among the earliest uses of kites was that of a lookout tower – a tower of variable height, without walls or stairs, a dancing, tossing belvedere on a leash.'

This man-lifting use of kites was, among other more theatrical activities, the trade of showman Samuel Franklin Cody, who prided himself on having the same surname as his famous colleague Bill Cody, better known as Buffalo Bill. In fact he loved it if people mistook him for his namesake. In 1901 Cody patented a box kite for military use. It took him quite an amount of effort to sell his idea to the English army, as they saw his attempts to present it as just an extension of his stunt man status. A flight across the Channel, whereby a special boat pulled him, finally convinced the military. After a few years, however, the kite had to

Some Japanese kites are so enormous and heavy that it takes several hundred people to fly them.

strong material. It provides privacy and shadow and does indeed absorb infrared radiation, instead of letting it through to irritate the occupants. Furthermore the loose weave allows heat to disperse. The temperature difference between the inside and the outside can be as much as 30 degrees Celsius. Because the textile is made of hair it also provides insulation against the cold. Faegre's amazement about a tent concept, that originated in desert country, spreading all the way to the icy mountains is fully understandable.

For desert use the tent is made almost flat. The cloth that Bedouins use, consists of several breadths sewn together. The total lengths may differ from six metres

make way for the airplane.

Kites gracefully exist by the grace of tension. Until 35 years ago their construction always involved a framework, to take the bending forces caused by the fabric or paper, that in its turn absorbed the tension caused by the air pressure. And let us not forget the line that keeps the kite in the air. In the Far East it may even be a thick rope, that has to be held by several hundred people.

In 1963 the American Domina C. Jalbert succeeded in building a kite without a framework, the so called parafoil. Fabric, or foil, is stitched together in such a way, that air pressure provides it with the right wing-like shape to fly. It is the ultimate tension structure, as no compression is involved whatsoever. It does need a few whiffs of air.

Showman Samuel Franklin Cody, who loved to be mistaken for his famous namesake Buffalo Bill, demonstrates his kite design to the British army in 1904.

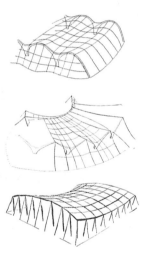

in hot weather the tent is left open.

Many variations exist due to different weather conditions. For instance the roof may be built up steeper in case of rain. The Durrani tribe uses hoops of bent wood to support the roof and the Lur cover their tents with mud. They only live in them part of the year and return to the same spot every time, so the tents can be left in place.

Basically the draped tent is the most primitive kind of dwelling, except for the cave. It consists of a frame of dug in sticks with animal skins on top. Since its origin it has developed into more elaborate constructions, some of which serve as permanent housing. In Somalia the usual shape is a dome that is covered with mats made out of palm leaves.

Yurts, mainly used by the Mongols, are almost like houses. In fact many people inhabit them permanently or use them as a garden house next to their brick dwelling. They were invented in Central Asia and stand out in stability and construction. The walls are built with several so-called khana, each of which consists of 33 wooden shearing slats. In old yurts the hinges are made by simply lashing them together, but the current factory produced ones work with screws or rivets.

to over twenty, depending on the owners affluence. Tension bands are fixed across the breadths, each being supported by three poles, one in the middle and two on either side. Pitching a tent - generally a women's job - starts with fixing the cloth to the ground with stakes. Then one by one the poles are placed, first the ones on one side, then ones in the middle and so on. After that all the walls are pinned to the roof, but

Unfolded they look like old fashioned garden fences about two metres long.

To build the yurt, the khana – typically six or eight – are placed in a circle, on either side of a wooden door frame. The lattice segments are leashed together. Next the roof frame, a bent wooden crown with roof poles attached to it is placed on the lattice. The roof and walls are then tied together.

If the frame construction was left like this it would collapse under the weight of the felt coverings. This is prevented ingeniously by one woven tension band tied around the top of the wall. The frame can be covered with layers of felt, a material unequalled in its capability of keeping bad weather outside. Sometimes the top layer is oiled. In modern yurts the roof felt may be placed sandwich-wise in between two layers of canvas. Living in yurts involves rituals. Among the Kazakhs these are inherited from one generation to the next. Everything in the tent has its own traditional place. The place of honour is near the hearth. It is the spot where the best carpets are laid down. Ritual often has a functional rationale behind it. Karakalpak children, for example, were allowed to swing on a rope that was hung from the crown of the roof. This caused the construction to settle.

As tents were the first building constructions they served as examples for the building of more permanent housing. That transition may have happened slowly. As we have seen some tribes cover their tents with mud. From there on it is only a small step to brick or stone buildings.

Particularly the lightness of tensile tents has recently gained the interest of architects, especially those who are involved in developing prefabricated extended covering constructions. Renzo Piano often applies tent like roofing and Frei Otto is a dedicated tent roof ana-

The yurt is a very successful tent concept. It has existed for a long time and is now produced in small factories.

'The yurt is held together by the same principle as the Extra 400 fuselage.'

HIGH RISE CLIMATE CONTROL

In Yemen the typical city consists of age old buildings that may be as high as eight storeys. The ancient city of Shibam in the south of the country is called Manhattan of the desert because of this. The loamy walls of these apartment towers are very good at regulating room temperature and not just because they are two to three metres thick. In contrast to the fabric of black tents, that simply allows hot air to escape, they provide the buildings with material inherent water cooling. When the walls cool down through the night, they absorb water from the air, that can be quite moist, even in cool desert conditions. During daytime the water evaporates, absorbing the superfluous heat in the process, which cools the walls down. It is a different way of integrating multiple functions in one material, one very heavy composite material this time.

lyst. He is convinced of the importance of tension to minimize the amount of material in cover structures and he has developed some interesting ideas on cable nets. By combining and spanning parallel sets of cables he has designed pseudo-tent constructions, that differ from real ones in the sense that there is no fabric involved. One layer of parallel cables is spanned between thicker cables or within a stiff frame structure on top of another one in a more or less perpendicular direction. The shapes that come out of this procedure are different from those in classic tents, as they are not determined by interaction of material under tension and gravity, but by one set of spanned cables deforming another. They do indeed look exciting because of this. The disadvantage is that load can only be absorbed in the direction of the cables, as a result of which the constructions involve more weight. In the case of the Olympic Stadium in Munich the roofing is made to look light through the use of transparent plastic tiles. Architects often are more interested in the image of lightness, than in lightness itself. <

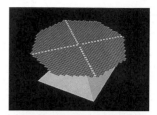

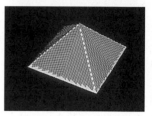

Exploring
expression

The Germans found a way to wrap six egg cups with foil that is not unlike the way the Japanese pack five eggs.

Plastics, and composites too, don't just support human needs as the material part of the trinity – material, shape and process – that defines functional structures. They also have a feel to them, they produce certain sounds when touched and they have their own looks, so much so, that for instance lacquer and print can provide the illusion that something is made out of carbon fibre reinforced polymers, when actually it is not. All in all plastics and composites have got their characteristic expression, like any other material. They also have a slight identity problem. From the very beginning of industrialization plastics have been used to replace other materials. They served to rationalize production and were made to look like ivory, wood or lacquered metal in the same way that, these days, metal products are sometimes produced in the guise of carbon. They have hardly had the chance to prove themselves from the esthetic point of view. One way to find out more about the character of plastics, is artisan experimentation.

Some of this did occur in the Yelling Sixties. Industrial designers and architects started to discover the endless possibilities and began to experiment with polyester and rubbery polyurethane. They made the first inflatable chairs and pneumatic buildings and the first one piece injection moulded plastic furniture. It was a colourful feast of plastic expression that slowly ebbed away. Plastic gradually got a bad name among

EIERBECHER
6 Stück EVP M 2,10

'Open-mindedness and daring to be vulnerable provide designers with the strength to create something unexpected.'

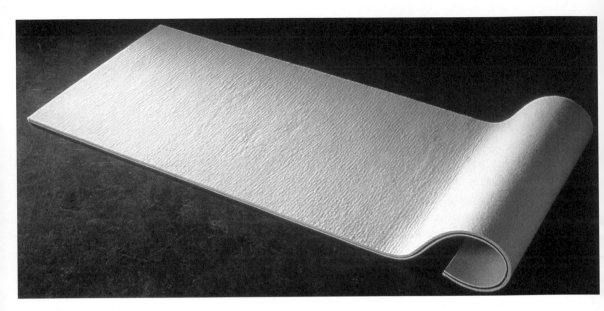

Martijn Hoogendijk: 'Wave'.
Glaze-melted traditional felt with polyurethane and polyester fibres.

designers, because many plastic products were of inferior quality, partly due to lack of knowledge and partly to disinterest among producers. Moreover the environment changed from something we took for granted into something that one had to care for. Much of the ever growing flow of waste consisted of plastics, for despite their bad image plastics and their markets kept on growing.

Over the past few years the attention to plastics has been renewed. Designers are experimenting again. Under the name 'Droog Design' some work by young Dutch designers has become famous throughout the world. Droog Design is a foundation, started five years ago by art historian Renny Ramakers and designer Gijs Bakker. Their aim is to present Dutch design on an international platform to provoke discussion within the design community. The only common denominator is that the objects must be 'droog', which simply is the Dutch word for 'dry'. Droog design can be considered typically Dutch in that the presented objects are uncomplicated and obvious. Everyone understands them. But at the same time they are foxy and ironic creations with a strong intriguing presence. Beauty is paradoxically achieved by carefully avoiding any styling attempts.

One of the designs, made by Hella Jongerius, was a vase with a classic shape and a deliberate artisanal imperfection made out of soft rubbery poly-urethane. It was the immediate cause to start the Dry-tech project, in which several designers would participate in experimenting with high-tech fibre based materials. When asked, Adriaan Beukers immediately placed

'Industrial designers seem te be out of control, but they are not.'

SITTING ON
A STRONG IDEA

Wanders' knotted chair, now both part of the collection of the Museum of Modern Art in New York and of Central Museum In Utrecht, is the most successful result of the 'Dry-tech' project. It is made by first macraméing the basic structure with a supple braid, especially wrought out of carbon (for the core) and aramid fibres. The result of the knotting procedure is a slack net that is drenched with plastic resin. Next the fabric is hung within a cube-like metal frame, like laundry. Gravity creates the chair shape, in exactly the same way that Gaudí used to determine the structure of his buildings. The chair's form is ultimately fixed by hardening the resin. Finally the finished chair is detached from the frame.

The strangest question Marcel Wanders got when he explained the making of the chair to an exhibition visitor was: 'How on earth can you tie knots in this extremely stiff material?' Apparently the technology is too straightforward to be understood. According to the designer industry technicians were stunned when they first saw the construction.

For Wanders the chair is a real winner: 'It has a lot to offer in that it strongly and respectfully appeals to all kinds of people. It can be considered warm and old fashioned, as well as modern and aesthetic. Everyone touches it and everybody has an opinion about it. It is impossible to neglect. Some designers tend to disagree with the concept. That too is something I wanted to achieve. The chair generates discussion.'

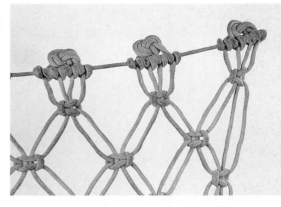

his knowledge and the material research laboratory of his Faculty at their disposal.

It led to an interesting confrontation between technology oriented people and the Dry Tech expressionists, because their approaches are very different and, because of that, mutually enriching. For instance Jongerius in her uninhibited way put a test object in the oven to see what would happen. She didn't care if it deformed or even burned, because to her that was at least as fascinating as calculated perfection. Technical researchers tend to try and prevent mishaps by reasoning. Designers, at least some of them, have a totally different perception of success. They're looking for other answers.

The first edition of the Dry-tech project resulted in three interesting objects that were first shown in Milan in 1996. Two of them were inspired by the same material being hard and soft, depending on treatment. Martijn Hoogendijk came up with a floormat to lie on with a built in leaning support. It consisted of two layers of felt reinforced with a layer of poly-urethane in between. It could be rolled up around the support that only distinguished itself from the rest of the mat by its

curved shape. The support was made stiff by choosing a different composition of the elastomer.

Whereas glass fibres are usually made into non-wovens or wovens, Hella Jongerius tried to knit it, and succeeded. She made four knitted lamps consisting of knitted glass and perspex. The glass fitted like a sweater around the light bulbs and diffused the light in a novel way. Marcel Wanders designed the third object, the knotted chair, that proved extremely successful. The Italian furniture producer Capellini now sells it.

The 1997 edition was a little less convincing, but still very interesting. Hella Jongerius made two stools out of fibre and poly-urethane, each consisting of two cylinders with a soft one on the outside and a stiff one inside. To make them she applied a random fibre coiling technique. The resulting objects were impregnated with the plastic. For one she used an aramid fibre and for the other a entirely new fibre, mysteriously called M5. It has a strange peacock blue gleam and is reputed to be just as strong as carbon, but less brittle. Wanders expanded on his knotted chair ideas by designing two small beam like coffee tables made out

of transparent epoxy resin curiously reinforced with white lace.

Two other designers, Jan Konings and Jurgen Bey, ended up not using fibres at all. But they did find an inspiring application for a sprayable PVC-grade that is normally used to pack military equipment and airplanes when they are not in use. It behaves a bit like a cross between textile and chewing gum when sprayed and is able to fill up openings because of this. They had it sprayed on old wooden chairs. The plastic skin shrinks in a special way and thereby provides existing chairs with an unprecedented shape and expression. Their aim is to combine existing pieces of furniture and maybe other objects, like boxes, into new ones by fitting them into one skin. It needs lots of experimentation to unveil the characteristics of shape that evolves from a skin that shrinks itself into tension and covers openings. <

Left: Hella Jongerius coiled fibres at random and impregnated them with polyurethane. She also can be considered the first person to knit lamps with glass. Top: With the spider web technique Konings and Bey make new furniture out of old chairs.

For some reason we've become accustomed to packing fluids and gases in containers that are disproportionately heavy. Small amounts of fluid are often transported in glass bottles. In the region of hundreds of litres we generally put milk, beer and chemical liquids in metal tanks. Gases are practically always stored in steel containers. As a result of this, liquid and gaseous substances are transported with tremendous inefficiency, especially if we consider the fact that all that is needed to contain them is a strong impervious flexible skin.

Luckily it seems that the days of heavy and noisy tanks are over. Glass bottles are slowly being displaced by plastic ones and recently it was suggested that, to transport water overseas, it doesn't have to be loaded into a ship, but can be contained in an extremely large plastic bag instead. It will keep afloat by itself. Moreover, most current gasoline tanks for automobiles consist of plastic. The Laboratory for Structures and Materials in Delft has delved into possibilities of changing the metal con-

tainer concept with composite materials and come up with some quite promising solutions, for liquids as well as for gases. In terms of the trinity they are all based on continuous fibres wound in an iso-tensoid structure. In the case of containers this means that tensile stress in all skin fibres is constant when they are filled up.
Not all filled skins are iso-tensoid. It depends on the shape that results when they are under full pressure. The best example is a drop of fluid with a certain surface tension, that forces it into an iso-tensoid shape. Cushions or, more extremely cubes don't allow even distribution of stress in their skin. They can be produced, but they always tend to wrinkle at certain spots. The beach tourist tribe, playing around with the most remarkable inflatable contraptions, doesn't mind the wrinkles. In the blowing Sixties many architects

FLYING BY TENSION
Many an ambitious balloon has fallen out of thin air lately. The French brothers Montgolfier made the first one out of linen and paper in 1783. Pilatre de Rozier and the Marquis d'Arlandes used a Montgolfier balloon to make the first manned flight in Paris. It flew because the hot air inside has a lower density than the surrounding air. Later that same year French chemist J. A. C. Charles inflated a balloon with hydrogen and launched it in that same city. Hydrogen is superior to hot air for filling a balloon, since its buoyancy doesn't depend on heating and fuel. The much safer gas helium (not

flammable) did not become commercially available until after 1918. All the inventors, pioneers and cheering people watching probably didn't realize that the balloon is a perfect tensegrity structure. The gas inside is tamed by one continuous layer of thin material, that exclusively has to withstand tension stress. The iso-tensoid structure was still unknown, but the obvious spherical shape, that must have evolved naturally from the first experiments, comes pretty close.
Once launched, a balloon will rise until its average density exactly equals that of the surrounding atmosphere. In order to go higher, the pilot must discard some ballast (bags of sand are often used). To descend, the pilot releases some of the buoyant gas through a

Virgin boss Richard Branson lost his balloon even before he could start his jet stream world tour.

The Belgian artist Panamarenko is famous for his visionary non-flying machines that express lightness beautifully. He made a transparent cross between a balloon and a blimp and killed it with scissors as soon as it started to rise. It was never supposed to fly.

valve. When the balloon lands, a ripping panel is opened to allows the remaining gas to escape. The balloon was put into early use by the military to observe the battlefield and direct artillery fire. When the Austrians besieged Venice in 1849, they used 200 small hot-air balloons to bomb the area. Because of unpredictable winds the results were negligible.
The spherical balloon was excellent if it could go where the wind took it, but leashed to the ground it had trouble with its anchor cables. By 1900, sausage-shaped balloons had been developed that behaved more predictable from the aerodynamic point of view. They can be considered the first zeppelins. Extremely high-altitude balloons are used by astronomers and physicists to detect cosmic rays and gamma rays arriving from outer space. These balloons are sometimes several hundred metres tall, and their reusable instrument packages are returned to Earth by parachute. Development of very thin, tough balloon materials such as Astrofilm E

The LPG tank's inner skin is wound with glass to tame the pressure. In the final product carbon fibres will be used instead.

accelerated such balloon use in the 1980s.
The great dream of 19th-century balloonists was intercontinental air travel. It has remained so until this day. There is a one million dollar award for the first hero to balloon around the world in a single flight. A multiple of that amount has been spent on failed attempts.

were infested with gale force inflatomania and built complete buildings out of foil and air. The craze has gone by, but inflatable structures are still being developed, albeit on a rather more sensitive level.
The ball or wheel shaped containers that are under development in Delft can be considered two-dimensional tensegrity structures, as tensile stress is absorbed by one continuous element. One could even speak of 'compressegrity', since the element that absorbs the pressure - the contained substance - is continuous too.
Until the 50s beer was transported in wooden barrels. From then on rustproof steel or aluminium barrels took over. This meant a true revolution in the brewery world:

LIGHT
WEIGHT LIFTERS

Try this at home: lay a plastic garbage bag on a table. Put somebody on top, or maybe a heavy dog, and start blowing up the bag. Do it slowly, or you'll get dizzy. You will see that the person or the animal will be lifted. A little air pressure does the trick. The only problem is that it will be difficult for the volunteer on

because of diminishing perishability beer, and other beverages as well, could be transported over great distances. Over the past ten years lighter plastic containers have appeared on the market, but their ability to maintain quality is inferior to that of metal.

In beer transport the container skin must stop oxygen from entering the container, as this gas would turn the expression 'one pint of bitter' into a nasty truth for all kinds of beer. At the same time carbon acid must be kept inside. Apart from that the material must be strong enough to withstand pressure. To fulfil these demands the only possibility is to apply the 'bag-in-box' concept. It entails two skins. There is one inside skin to take care of the imperviousness and one around it to absorb the stresses. The outer one consists of a fibre reinforced flexible material.

The estimated reduction of transport volume is 25 percent. Apart from that a container is flexible, saving space during return transport. After use the inner skin is taken out for recycling and replaced. To tap beer, or any other drink, pressure is built up between the inner

top of the bag to keep their balance.

With more pressure inflatable cushions can be used to lift extremely heavy bodies, even if they weigh somewhere in the region of 120 tons. Best results are achieved of course with an iso-tensoid structure with strong fibres embedded in a thin rubber layer. The optimum shape resembles that of a wheel or rather a Dutch cheese.

The advantage is its stability, especially when a number of them are stacked on top of each other. Truck drivers can use these light and compact lifting bodies to change a truck tire. They usually have compressed air at their disposal. The best composite pressure vessel is a solid of revolution with a coiling angle for the fibres that can be calculated with a special formula.

'The combination of displacing volume and flexible surface can exert enormous forces.'

LOGISTIC PUZZLES

Milk cans, hay, pigs, a drawer chest, his grandfather: a farmer can load anything on his wagon, take it to town and bring back groceries and even a piano if necessary. Specialization on the other hand, can be very limiting indeed. Most modern trucks are not as versatile as they should be. It is true that many trailers are fit to carry different loads, but a cooling trailer can't transport unbottled milk or gasoline, nor can a tanker carry clothes.

This is where flexible containers come in handy. If fluids or gases are stored in 'bags' that are easily folded, they can be transported on the same trailer that can hold anything else, provided of course that it is not too big. The main advantage is that a trailer that has brought a load of parcel goods to a certain city, can return partly filled with fluids and partly with food instead of empty. Now we really start talking logistics.

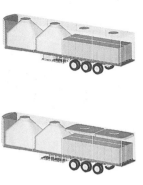

and the outer skin. As the inside skin is impervious to oxygen this can be done with air, with a simple compressor. Transport of carbon acid cylinders is no longer necessary.

A consumer version is currently under development. The contents of an entire crate is reduced to a small ball that easily fits in the fridge. The end user will be able to pressurize the inner container with tap water. Of course the use of skin to pack fluids is not at all new. Wine and water have been, and still are, contained by animal skin, a very versatile material. It is even air tight. Ancient reliefs show that Assyrians used air filled goat skins to keep themselves afloat in the water.

Therefore the same packing principle used for beer can be applied to gases. The lab in Delft is working on an LPG fuel tank for cars. In the Netherlands and Italy approximately ten percent of all cars use LPG, a propane-butane mixture. The LPG markets in the UK and France are expected to grow rapidly in the years to come. There is a slight difference in the applied materials and the construction, since the pressure is much higher and the contained substance is different. Right now all LPG tanks in the Netherlands are made of

Assyrian warriors threatened by Assyrian archers make their way across the river floating on air filled goat skins.

Chinese farmers near the Zhongyuan oil fields in China's Henan province carry back to their homes giant plastic bags filled with natural gas stolen from wells along the road. They use the gas for cooking and heating, causing annual losses of more than 20 million yuan (5 million guilders) to the oil companies.

steel and most of them have a cylindrical shape that occupies a considerable part of the boot. That is why more and more LPG drivers want a ring shaped tank that fits in the well that is reserved for the spare wheel. Small cars in particular can benefit from this solution. Steel tanks are also quite heavy. A ring shaped one typically weighs 38 kilograms, more than one mechanic can or is allowed to handle. He has to get help from a colleague to mount it, which makes it more expensive. Moreover, a heavy tank is superfluous load that increases fuel consumption. For every 100 extra kilograms a car uses approximately 0.7 more litres every 100 kilometres. This may seem not all that dramatic, but the picture changes when we consider the increase for, say 1,000,000 cars. Suddenly we're talking about wasting the contents of twenty fully loaded tankers.

Originally the LPG container was to be flexible, like the

one for beer. This idea appeared to generate manufacturing problems. The market was low on acceptance
anyway. Now it consists of a stiff liner made of a new
impervious thermoplastic produced by Shell, called
Carilon. Carbon fibre is coiled around it to provide the
strength. In the middle the wheel shape is held flat by a
tension rod made out of a short fibre reinforced injection moulded thermoplastic. The whole object is
covered with a layer of two-component rubber for protection.
The new tank's weight is about 7.5 kilograms, no less
than 80 percent lighter than its steel competitor. This
weight reduction implies that environmental load is
reduced by the same amount. Currently the new
design is being tested for safety. Unexpected phenomena may occur. For instance when a partly filled tank is

heated at the bottom, the top is the part that becomes
hot, due to the fact that the vapourized LPG above the
fluid can reach a much higher temperature.
Experiences like this demonstrate just how crucial
prototype testing is. No structure can do without it,
however light it may be. <

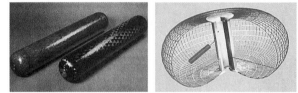

$$X = Y_i \sqrt{1 + 2q(1+r)} \left\{ \int_0^\theta \sqrt{1 - \frac{(q-1)\sin^2\theta}{1 + 2q(1+r)}} \, d\theta - \frac{1 + q(1+r)}{1 + 2q(1+r)} \int_0^\theta \left(1 - \frac{(q-1)\sin^2\theta}{1 + 2q(1+r)}\right)^{-1/2} d\theta \right\}$$

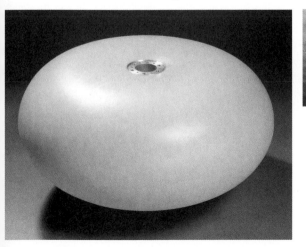

Left: For composite LPG containers
the cylinder is a less efficient shape
than the isotensoid. The chance for
explosions is reduced in comparison
with the metal solution.
Above: New generation design using
extended netting theory for optimum
weight.

The large main hall of the Laboratory for Structures and Materials in Delft is crammed with all kinds of airplane parts. To the visitor all the fuselage chunks, wing sections, tails and landing gear mainly are a reminder of the massive complexity of airplane structures as well as their primitiveness. According to Adriaan Beukers the airplane industry is still in its infancy.

'When mankind was still unable to fly, birds always were his greatest example. For centuries imitating them seemed the only way to reach for the sky. Then, around the beginning of this century, someone got the brilliant idea of separating the functions of lift, propulsion, stability and control.

'From that moment on inventors and engineers started to develop the airplane structure by analysis and on-going functional subdivisions: wings, engines, cockpit, cabin, windows, aluminium sheet, ribs and rivets. The current airplane structure is determined by what we were unable to do a hundred years ago. The process of specialization gradually made us drift away from the original dream.'

This is how Beukers describes the cause of a loss of universality and overview. It resulted in ongoing improvement of a concept that probably is not the best possible solution for flying at all. Designers and engineers should always open-mindedly return to the roots of the original overall problem and try to reach maximum results with minimum resources. This is Beukers' main motivation. He elaborates on it in this interview:

What is wrong with specialization? We have learned a great deal on many subjects, including airplane technology, and it is simply impossible to know everything.

'There are two kinds of researchers. The connoisseurs know very much about very little. They tend to work on small isolated islands and find it difficult to communicate. The collectioneurs are the opposite. They have a wider scope and try to relate ideas to one another. Unfortunately they are a minority.

'The specialism of connoisseurs is often crippling, because their scientific activity is introverted. Not communicating about ideas and seeking individual expertise on details so tiny that they are on the verge of being irrelevant, provides a feeling of safety. The same ideas are reinvented over and over again. Take for instance the finite elements method for checking mechanical behaviour by computing. It is 30 years old. The theory of laminates for composites is even older: 80 years. Nevertheless in every scientific article that remotely concerns these practices, they are explained as if they are new phenomena. If scientific articles are dominated by the list of references at the end – many of them are –, this implies they are virtually identical. To tell the truth I have stopped reading them.

'The performance of universities currently is measured in quantity rather than quality. The ideal seems to be not to provide good education and insight, but the production of an ever increasing output of publications by young affordable professors without students or a laboratory. Moreover it has been a historic mistake to separate different kinds of universities, for they can inspire one another and exchange knowledge and experience. Historians or economists, for instance, may benefit from technical knowledge and vice versa. Technology is part of our culture, no less than music or the study of languages.

'Scientific practice has become rigid and conservative. Tendencies and intuition are considered unscientific. Researchers are not supposed to explore ideas, but to look for certainties. Where doubt is excluded breakthroughs are completely ruled out. Research and development are terrorized by people with a closed mind who have been working for 30 years. One reason why wooden airplanes lost all of their territory to their metal successors was not because they were inferior, but because behaviour of metal was easier to predict with scientific methods. Metal is so homogeneous and well-behaved, that simple calculations match reality. Applicability of theoretic formulas has become a quality in itself, which, I think, is silly.'

Do you think the same thing is true for the application of technical standards? I mean you have said more than once that they hamper technological development.

'Well, in a slightly different sense it is. Standards always run after the facts. Safety standards confirm what you shouldn't do, but they don't say what you have to do. Generally there is too much emphasis on their literal meaning. They should be interpreted in spirit, like a good lawyer interprets laws. Maybe technical standards should be written by philosophers instead of technicians, in order for them to represent their essence instead of superficial descriptions with a limited scope.'

Does all this imply that you advocate a more practical approach to design and construction?

'Yes absolutely, more practical, more open and more vulnerable. I used to love listening to freethinkers on the radio, mainly because they had the guts to say stupid things. There is a difference between science and design, that is often neglected. Design is not guided by the quest for certainty, but by the desire to create and to solve problems. Good designers are open to the world around them. They have the ability to absorb and associate freely, come up with any idea and see if it works. They thrive on uncertainty and are stimulated by it. It makes them conquer something. They are anti-sectarian. Design is a process of integration, whereas science often involves retreat into a small world of analysis that is often meaningless with respect to the total.

'Design is also a matter of craftsmanship. You should have a feeling for materials and structures and the way they behave, that is based on experience – you should literally be in touch with technology. Some time ago a friend of mine had a garage and as a mechanic he knew how to think ahead. For example, he carefully put grease on nuts and bolts to make sure they wouldn't corrode and could be loosened when the car was returned for next year's servicing. He was a bit like a Chinese doctor, who gets paid when he keeps you healthy, instead of when he cures you after you have fallen ill. Unfortunately his craftsmanship was not expressed in a diploma, so the garage had to be closed. 'This kind of craftsman's feeling for materials seems to be disappearing. Manufacturing has become a matter of assembly and all the parts are automatically produced, without human intervention. The result is that our acquaintance with materials and their idiosyncrasies is weakening.'

So if you think engineers should be more in touch with what they are creating, what is the meaning of the use of computers?

'The computer is a fantastic tool. It does an enormous amount of slave labour, the kind of work that used to be done by hundreds of people with mechanical calculating machines. Because of electronic computing verification of ideas is much quicker and easier than it used to be. A problem arises when people start thinking that this calculating slave is an able designer, or when all this computing is turned into a goal, instead of a means to an end. Machines are not willing to learn or interpret. They have no open mind, but they are indeed of great help.

'The danger is that this great calculating ability is mistaken for reality. I urge all the students in this Laboratory to get away from their computers screens every know and then, to experiment with real materials and constructions.'

You have obviously developed into a practical man. What is your background concerning your interest in composite materials?

'Well, I graduated in the 1970s on a theoretical subject, something difficult with stress distributions, involving complex mathematics. But then composites announced themselves and I decided to get to know more about them, in a practical sense that is. I had a strong feeling they had a future in airplane constructions.

'My fascination for airplanes developed rather romantically when I was a kid. The way people fly is so unnatural that it becomes a miracle. My father had a job at KLM and he used to take me to Schiphol Airport to have a look around inside airplanes. I really liked the smell of hydraulic oil, upholstery, paint and pilot's sweat. The reason I took up studying came about after high school, when I spent a few years in Italy. That made me realize that I had to have an education to be able to make the money to have a good life. My interest in composites originated from my teacher, professor Spies. He was a charismatic man and he was the one who gave me the chance to start working on composites at Fokker.

'The funny thing is that as a student I had decided never to apply for a job at Fokker, for it seemed like some sort of prison to me. After graduating I was accepted at TNO, a Dutch research institution, to work on vibration in steel constructions. I didn't like the idea of letting go of composites. This I told to professor Spies and the next day I got a call from Fokker. I gladly accepted, even though it really was like a prison.

'It was an extremely bureaucratic organization. For instance you weren't allowed to start working on a project before the budget had an official number, with the result that engineers did nothing for days on end. Consequently product development only got a chance in the informal circuit. I worked at Fokker for seven or eight years and after that I started in Delft.'

Was it troublesome to acquire the freedom you have now?

'Not at all. It is far more difficult to maintain it. People are constantly messing around in your kitchen. The hard thing is to keep away those who are constantly putting claims on you, how ever nice they may be. I like to start something new every couple of years. I want to be able to breathe freely. When people start clinging to me I change direction.

'Many things are lying around waiting to be dealt with. That is also why one in every four graduates can start a company. They can drop by without costs. They are an important asset to our economy. Keeping an old airplane industry like Fokker alive would be nostalgia, but exploitation of knowledge is very profitable. It represents the best value added. It is far better to develop and export knowledge services and advanced products than to do the ordinary. The Netherlands should be a country of creative engineering and manufacturing companies. Activities like distribution of as many tons of goods as possible are by no means big moneymakers. We should learn to think in terms of added value rather than kilograms. Our Dutch trading spirit is counterproductive in this sense.'

Could politics play a role in promoting the idea of lightness and the selling of knowledge regarding light structures?

'It could do so by simple rules, such as all cars have to weigh less than 1000 kilograms by the year so and so. Government should be more active. Unfortunately politicians tend to suppress daring. They should listen more to their policymakers. I am often surprised by their broad strategic vision. Implementation of ideas is more our business.

'That is where composites come in. The time is ripe for them. They provide us with a tremendous opportunity. All infrastucture for development is available in the Netherlands. Metals really gained their superiority by excellent reproducible mechanical properties. For composites something similar may occur because of their thermal and acoustic properties, or rather their ability to combine different functions. Metal airplane structures have to be made tons heavier just to compensate for acoustic effects, whereas composites can solve this problem by themselves. They can be tailored to requirements, which ironically appears advantageous in comparison with the uniformity and the predictability of metal.

'Composites, combined with electronics and control engineering provide us with the chance to return to the old ideal of imitating birds. We can do virtually anything now.' <

In depth

MATERIALS AND FUNCTION

The most important thing to do when choosing a material for a certain function is to keep an open mind. In his book on materials selection Ashby proposes several quick and easy selection procedures. One of them deals with materials and function, regardless of shape. Materials have many properties: density, strength, thermal conductivity, cost, etcetera. The choice of the right combination of properties can be quite difficult. An easy way out is the use of a performance index, a formula to calculate the best solution.

This example from his book of course presents an overview of criteria for minimizing weight. The lightest combination of properties depends on geometry and failure mode. The largest possible calculated value for the formulas represents a minimum weight solution. Two failure modes have been selected: excessive elastic deflection (including buckling) and plastic collapse, for a number of different materials. Some variables are free. In the case of tension (ties) the

Performance-maximizing property groups

mode of loading		minimize weight for given	
		stiffness	ductile strength
Tie (tensile strut) F, l specified r free		$\dfrac{E}{\rho}$	$\dfrac{\sigma_f}{\rho}$
Torsion bar T, l specified r free		$\dfrac{G^{1/2}}{\rho}$	$\dfrac{\sigma_f^{2/3}}{\rho}$
Torsion tube T, l, r specified t free		$\dfrac{E^{1/2}}{\rho}$	$\dfrac{\sigma_f^{2/3}}{\rho}$
Bending of rods and tubes F, l specified r or t free		$\dfrac{E^{1/2}}{\rho}$	$\dfrac{\sigma_f^{2/3}}{\rho}$
Bucking of slender column or tube F, l, specified r or t free		$\dfrac{E^{1/2}}{\rho}$	-

Performance-maximizing property groups

mode of loading		minimize weight for given	
		stiffness	ductile strength

section can vary. Bending (beams) allows free but proportional choice of width and depth. Plates can have any thickness, and so on. It's all in the table.

mode of loading		minimize weight for given	
		stiffness	ductile strength
Bending of plate F, *l*, w specified t free		$\dfrac{E^{1/3}}{\rho}$	$\dfrac{\sigma_f^{1/2}}{\rho}$
Buckling of plate F, *l*, w specified t free		$\dfrac{E^{1/3}}{\rho}$	-
Cylinder with internal pressure P, r specified t free		$\dfrac{E}{\rho}$	$\dfrac{\sigma_f}{\rho}$
Rotating cylinder w, r specified t free		$\dfrac{E}{\rho}$	$\dfrac{\sigma_f}{\rho}$
Sphere with internal pressure p, r specified t free	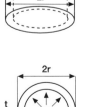	$\dfrac{E}{(1-v)\,\rho}$	-

specific properties	material	E/ρ $(10^6 \cdot m^2/s^2)$	$E^{1/2}/\rho$ $(m^{5/2}/s \cdot kg^{1/2})$	$E^{1/3}/\rho$ $(m^{8/3}/s^{2/3} \cdot kg^{2/3})$	σ/ρ $(10^3 \cdot m^2/s^2)$	$\sigma^{2/3}/\rho$ $(m^{7/3}/s^{4/3} \cdot kg^{1/3})$	$\sigma^{1/2}/\rho$ $(m^{5/2}/s \cdot kg^{1/2})$
metal	steel 0.2 carbon quenched	27	59	0.8	99	108	3.6
	steel: piano wires/springs	27	59	0.8	397	273	7.1
	aluminium 2024 T3	25	94	1.5	98	15	6
animal*	bovine bone	11	72	1.3	121	191	7.6
	ivory	9.2	70	1.4	114	190	7.8
	buffalo horn	2.0	40	1.1	95	191	8.6
	sinew	0.95	27	0.8	79	169	7.8
hardwood*	birch	25	198	3.9	211	409	18
	Wych elm	20	190	4.0	191	405	19
	ash	19	168	3.4	239	436	19
	oak	19	165	3.4	141	306	14
	elm	15	182	4.2	148	362	18
softwood*	scots pine	22	216	4.7	193	433	21
	taxus brevifolia	16	159	3.4	184	378	17
natural fibres*	jute	12	88	1.7	411	48	17
	flax	41	160	2.5	909	80	24
	sisal	35	161	2.7	526	59	20
	hemp	19	113	2.1	490	54	18
	coir	4.8	62	1.5	177	29	12
	cotton	4.3	47	1.1	430	49	17
synthetic fibres	HM-Carbon (M40)	214	342	4.0	1500	107	29
	HT-Carbon (T300)	131	272	3.5	2010	132	34
	HM-Aramid	78	232	3.3	2410	159	41
	S/R-Glass	36	120	1.8	1850	111	27
	E-Glass	28	105	1.6	1340	88	23

grey values = properties are only of academical importance
* = average values

specific properties

material		E/ρ $(10^6 \cdot m^2/s^2)$	$E^{1/2}/\rho$ $(m^{5/2}/s \cdot kg^{1/2})$	$E^{1/3}/\rho$ $(m^{8/3}/s^{2/3} \cdot kg^{2/3})$	σ/ρ $(10^3 \cdot m^2/s^2)$	$\sigma^{2/3}/\rho$ $(m^{7/3}/s^{4/3} \cdot kg^{1/3})$	$\sigma^{1/2}/\rho$ $(m^{5/2}/s \cdot kg^{1/2})$
metal	steel 0.2 carbon quenched	27	59	0.8	99	108	3.6
	steel: piano wires/springs	27	59	0.8	397	273	7.1
	aluminium 2024 T3	25	94	1.5	98	15	6
animal*	bovine bone	11	72	1.3	121	191	7.6
	ivory	9.2	70	1.4	114	190	7.8
	buffalo horn	2.0	40	1.1	95	191	8.6
	sinew	0.95	27	0.8	79	169	7.8
hardwood*	birch	25	198	3.9	211	409	18
	Wych elm	20	190	4.0	191	405	19
	ash	19	168	3.4	239	436	19
	oak	19	165	3.4	141	306	14
	elm	15	182	4.2	148	362	18
softwood*	scots pine	22	216	4.7	193	433	21
	taxus brevifolia	16	159	3.4	184	378	17
natural fibres* "	jute	12	88	1.7	411	48	17
	flax	20	113	2.0	455	50	17
	sisal	17	114	2.1	263	37	14
	hemp	9.5	80	1.6	228	32	12
	coir	2.4	44	1.2	88	18	8
	cotton	2.2	33	0.9	215	31	12
synthetic fibres"	HM-Carbon (M40)	107	242	3.2	749	67	20
	HT-Carbon (T300)	65	193	2.8	1000	83	24
	HM-Aramid	39	164	2.6	1210	100	29
	S/R-Glass	18	85	1.4	925	70	19
	E-Glass	14	74	1.3	669	56	16

grey values = properties are only of academical importance
* = average values
" = fibres applied in unidirectional composites, fibre volume content 50%

BIGGER AND THINNER

Structures can be made lighter by using material where it is needed to deal with the stress at hand and by leaving it out where its contribution has no value. This can imply geometrical expansion, for instance in the case of bending. The picture on the right shows six stages in making truss constructions lighter. In every step the required bars are thinner. The most complicated (the so called 'Michell structure') is by far the lightest and bears a strong resemblance to the femoral bone.

The cross-section of a bar, or preferably a pipe, determines its moment of inertia and thereby its resistance to bending forces. The bending stiffness of a thin-walled pipe twice as thick as a square bar is the same, but its weight is 80 percent less (far right).

Michell structure

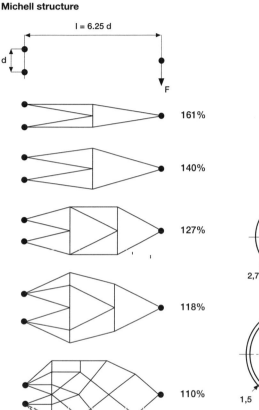

cross section   **weight**

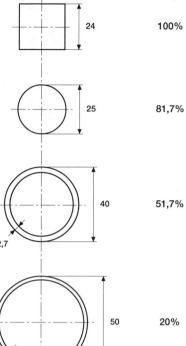

24	100%
25	81,7%
40 (2,7)	51,7%
50 (1,5)	20%

161%
140%
127%
118%
110%
100%

BUCKLING AND WEIGHT

Euler's theory of buckling, described in 'Compression champion', can easily be linked to the notion of material efficiency. The way to do this for the first case, in which the column is unclamped, is by specifying the moment of inertia in terms of thickness. After this the weight in relation to buckling strength is calculated by multiplying thickness, length and material density.
For the cases with one- and two-sided clamping, weight formulas can be derived in the same way.

the efficiency of columns under compression load

Euler buckling: $P_c = n \cdot \pi^2 \dfrac{E \cdot I}{L^2}$

E = Young's modulus
I = second moment of area of cross-section
L = length
n = support condition factor
t = cross-section characteristic dimension

suppose:

$I = c' \cdot t^4$

$W = c'' \cdot \rho \cdot t^2 \cdot L$

$\dfrac{P_c}{W} = \text{constant} \left(\dfrac{\sqrt{E}}{W} \right)^* \left(\dfrac{\sqrt{P}}{L^2} \right)''$

* = material efficiency criterion
'' = structure loading coefficient

P

P

the efficiency of panels under compression load

Euler buckling: $P_c = n \cdot \pi^2 \dfrac{E \cdot I}{L^2}$

E = Young's modulus
I = second moment of area of cross-section
L = length
n = support condition factor
t = panel thickness

suppose per unit width of panel:

$I = c' \cdot t^3$

$W = c'' \cdot \rho \cdot t \cdot L$

$\dfrac{P_c}{W} = \text{constant} \left(\dfrac{\sqrt[3]{E}}{\rho} \right)^* \left(\dfrac{\sqrt[3]{P^2}}{L^5} \right)''$

* = material efficiency criterion
'' = structure loading coefficient

OVERRULING WOOD

When people set their mind on something, it is extremely hard to make them reconsider. This, in brief, explains why metals took over from wood in the airplane industry in the period between the two world wars. Science historian Eric Schatzberg found that the main cause of metal supremacy in US aviation was an ideological choice. In fact it laid the basis for the current technological disadvantage of composites. Schatzberg argues that the choice between either of the two was not based on rational arguments: 'In the 1920s, the technical evidence favoured wood nor metal overall. Technical criteria thus cannot explain the aviation community's enthusiastic support for metal construction. In addition to technical arguments, supporters of metal invoked a nontechnical rhetoric that linked metal with progress and wood with stasis.'

In the world of airplane construction four factors were believed to determine the destiny of metal as the successor of wood: fire safety, weight, production costs and durability. This faith was not based on research or experience.

As for fire danger, the idea that metal airplanes were incombustible proved naive. In America the first commercial metal airplane was the German Junckers JL-6. The US Air Mail Services purchased eight of them and four were destroyed by flames, not because the metal caught fire, but because the fuel system didn't function properly. The metal structure was unable to deal with the heat.

Weight is a much more complicated issue as it depends on structural efficiency, which in its turn varies with the kind of load that different parts have to bear. It took enormous effort to build lighter metal airplanes. The saddest example is the DB-1 bomber, that turned out so heavy that the payload amounted to just about one hand grenade. A danger that metal airplane designers had to deal with was buckling. The invention of stressed-skin construction in the 1930s provided a streamlined external surface as well as a load-bearing structure, but it also made buckling more likely.

When the structural problems were finally solved, metal airplanes were still much more expensive to produce. The evasion of buckling took 'complex curved shapes, many different parts and a massive amount of riveting'. The reason that production of metal airplanes was not halted, was the firm belief that mass production would become cheaper in due time.

On durability Schatzberg remarks: 'Indeed, metals are in general more durable than wood, but both deteriorate when left unprotected.' In practice durability of metals was subject to a massive development effort and wood was simply neglected. It just didn't fit into the ideology. Schatzberg writes: 'Wood symbolized preindustrial technologies and craft traditions while metal represented the industrial age, technical progress, and the primacy of science.' For that was another reason why metals were preferred: they behave according to simple scientific rules, whereas wood doesn't.

At the end of his article the historian remarks: 'In recent years, nonmetallic materials have again found a place in airplane structures in the form of fibre-reinforced composites, of which wood is a natural example. Few aviation engineers, however, recognize the kinship between composite structures and the wooden airplanes of the past.'

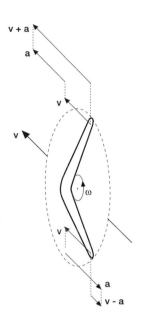

v + a
a
v
v
ω
v
a
v - a

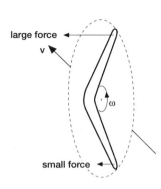

large force
v
ω
small force

precessional
velocity (Ω)

rotational
velocity (ω)

applied
torque (T)

BOOMERANGS

The characteristic movement of flying boomerangs is caused by several forces acting together. For a start, the velocity of a boomerang arm with respect to the air is not constant. When the arm points upward, the forward velocity of the boomerang adds to the velocity due to rotation (v + a, at the left), but when it points downward, these two velocities are in opposite directions. Consequently the resultant speed of the arm through the air will be smaller (v - a, at the left). Because of this, the aerodynamic force, which is directed from the flatter to the more convex side of the boomerang, is stronger when the arm points upward than when it points downward (centre). This implies that the average boomerang experiences not only a force from the right to the left, but also torque acting around a horizontal axis that tends to cant the boomerang with its upper part to the left. Moreover, because it is rapidly spinning it behaves like a gyroscope (which is simply a spinning flywheel with a free axis, at the right). When torque is exerted on a gyroscope, it does not give way, but instead changes its orientation around an axis that is perpendicular to both the axis of rotation and the axis of the applied torque. This motion is called precession. Similarly, the boomerang as a whole changes its orientation to the left.

THE LONGEST BRIDGE

Crossing the Strait of Gibraltar with a bridge is a challenging idea if there ever was one. The Swiss engineer Urs Meier proposed building one in an article in Proceedings from the Institution of Mechanical Engineers in 1987, with carbon fibre reinforced polymer cables.

On the basis of comparing specific design loads he concluded that a cable-stayed bridge would by far be the best solution: 'It is important to note that the material weight of the cables increases as the square of the span length for the suspension bridge as well as for the cable-stayed bridge. Therefore the saving of material with the cable-stayed criterion also applies for its superior stiffness. This undoubtedly proves that compared to suspension bridges, cable-stayed bridges are superior for all spans above approximately 200 metres.'

This is where he went wrong. The comparison is not fair since the main cables in a suspension bridge are 'loose hanging' catenaries, whereas the cables in a stayed bridge are pre-stressed, or they wouldn't be straight. This is necessary to provide the structure with sufficient stiffness. The implication is a loss of cable efficiency, since, apart from its own weight, the deck and the payload (traffic), the cable has to deal with the extra structural stress.

Maintaining Meier's assumptions that the specific design load (y) is constant for the entire bridge span and that the deck is flat and horizontal, calculations with updated material parameters - there have been improvements over the past ten years – show that, for y equals 0.5, the maximum span of a carbon cable-stayed bridge is a little under 3 kilometres. This is not enough to bridge the Strait. The carbon suspension bridge on the other hand would easily link Europe and Africa with a 12 kilometre span.

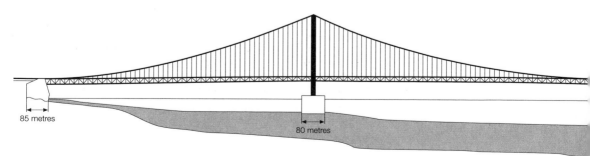

85 metres

80 metres

cable stayed bridge

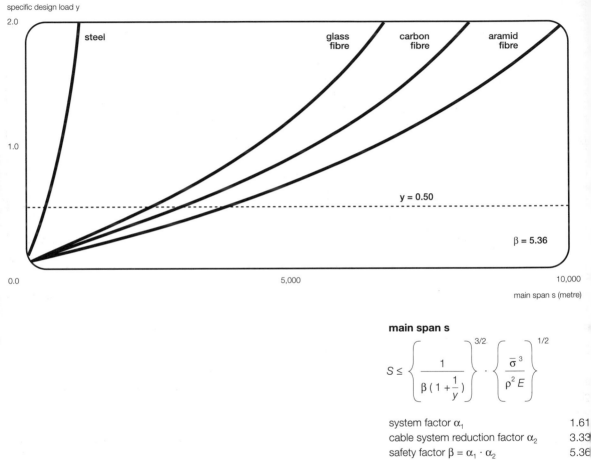

specific design load y

2.0

steel

glass fibre

carbon fibre

aramid fibre

1.0

y = 0.50

β = 5.36

0.0

5,000

10,000

main span s (metre)

main span s

$$S \leq \left\{ \frac{1}{\beta \left(1 + \frac{1}{y}\right)} \right\}^{3/2} \cdot \left\{ \frac{\overline{\sigma}^3}{\rho^2 E} \right\}^{1/2}$$

system factor α_1	1.61
cable system reduction factor α_2	3.33
safety factor $\beta = \alpha_1 \cdot \alpha_2$	5.36

$$Y = \frac{W_{cable}}{W_{deck} + W_{traffic}} \qquad W = \text{weight}$$

78 metres

80 metres

suspension bridge

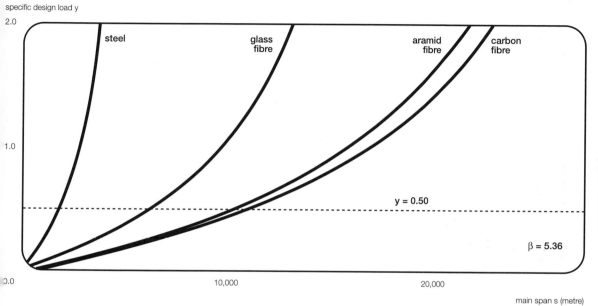

specific design load y

steel   glass fibre   aramid fibre   carbon fibre

y = 0.50

β = 5.36

main span s (metre)

pre-tension cable properties

	σ (10^6 N/m^2)	ρ (10^3 kgf/m^3)	E (10^9 N/m^2)
steel	1860	7.9	200
glass fibre	1700	2.1	50
carbon fibre	2400	1.7	140
aramid fibre	2000	1.5	70

fibre properties specified for UD-pultrusions with 60% fibre volume

main span s

$$S \leq \left\{ \frac{\lambda}{\beta \left(1 + \dfrac{1}{y}\right)} \right\} \cdot \left\{ \frac{\bar{\sigma}}{\rho \cdot g} \right\}$$

system factor α_1	1.61
cable system reduction factor α_2	3.33
safety factor $\beta = \alpha_1 \cdot \alpha_2$	5.36

classical catenary ($\bar{\sigma} / \sigma_0 = 1.81$) : $\lambda = 1.325$

suspension bridge versus cable stayed bridge

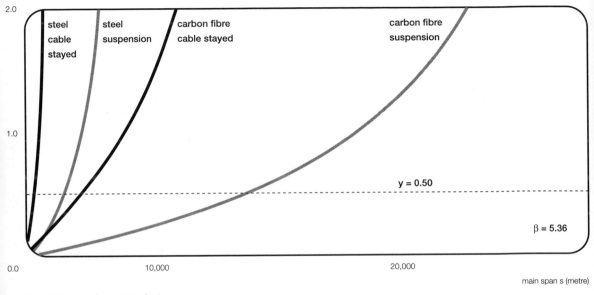

specific design load y

pre-tension cable properties

	σ (10^6 N/m^2)	ρ (10^3 kgf/m^3)	E (10^9 N/m^2)
steel	1860	7.9	200
carbon fibre	2400	1.7	140

fibre properties specified for UD-pultrusions with 60% fibre volume

maximum span s (metre); β = 5.36

specific design load	steel stayed	suspension	carbon fibre stayed	suspension
y = 0.25	160	1,190	1,330	7,120
y = 0.33	230	1,470	1,840	8,830
y = 0.50	**350**	**1,980**	**2,870**	**11,860**
⋮	⋮	⋮	⋮	⋮
y = inf.	1,830	5,990	14,890	35,580

"Cable stayed structures"

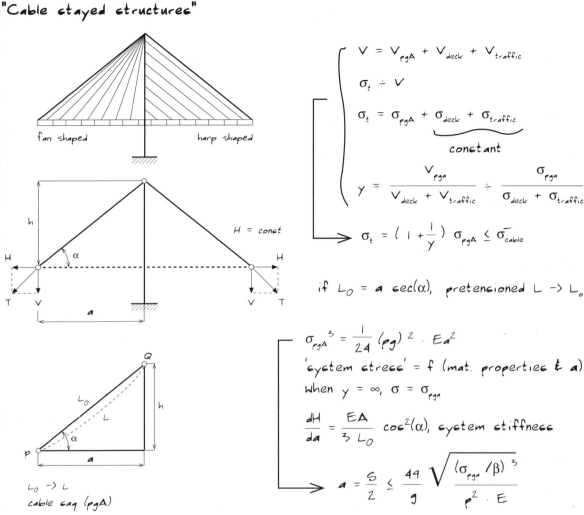

fan shaped   harp shaped

$H = const$

$L_0 \to L$
cable sag $(\rho g A)$

$$V = V_{\rho gA} + V_{deck} + V_{traffic}$$

$$\sigma_t \div V$$

$$\sigma_t = \sigma_{\rho gA} + \underbrace{\sigma_{deck} + \sigma_{traffic}}_{constant}$$

$$y = \frac{V_{\rho ga}}{V_{deck} + V_{traffic}} \div \frac{\sigma_{\rho ga}}{\sigma_{deck} + \sigma_{traffic}}$$

$$\sigma_t = \left(1 + \frac{1}{y}\right)\sigma_{\rho gA} \leq \bar{\sigma}_{cable}$$

if $L_0 = a \, \sec(\alpha)$, pretensioned $L \to L_0$

$$\sigma_{\rho gA}{}^3 = \frac{1}{24}(\rho g)^2 \cdot E a^2$$

'system stress' = f (mat. properties & a)

when $y = \infty$, $\sigma = \sigma_{\rho ga}$

$$\frac{dH}{da} = \frac{EA}{3 L_0}\cos^2(\alpha), \text{ system stiffness}$$

$$a = \frac{S}{2} \leq \frac{4.9}{g}\sqrt{\frac{(\sigma_{\rho ga}/\beta)^3}{\rho^2 \cdot E}}$$

$$\sigma_{\rho ga} = \frac{1}{1 + \frac{1}{y}}\bar{\sigma}_{cable}$$

β = system reduction factor

"Classical suspension bridge" – catenary or chain curve –

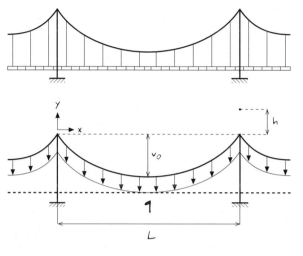

$$q = \underbrace{q_{egA} + q_{deck} + q_{traffic}}_{constant}$$

$$y = \frac{q_{ega}}{q_{deck} + q_{traffic}}, \quad 0 < y < \infty$$

$$q_{egA} = \rho \cdot g \cdot A_{cable}$$

$$\longrightarrow \quad q = \left(1 + \frac{1}{y}\right) q_{egA}$$

max. span L solution: $\quad y = h = 0 \quad x = L_0 = \dfrac{L}{2}$

$$v_0 = \frac{N_0}{q} \left\{ 1 - \cosh \frac{q L_0}{N_0} \right\} \qquad\qquad v = v_0 \text{ if } x = 0 \text{ or } x = L$$

$$N = N_0 \cosh \frac{q L}{2 N_0} \qquad\qquad\qquad\qquad N = N_0 \text{ if } x = L_0$$

$$L \le \frac{2\bar{\sigma}}{q/A_{cable}} \left\{ \frac{\sigma_0}{\bar{\sigma}} \cosh^{-1} \frac{\bar{\sigma}}{\sigma_0} \right\} \qquad \text{maximum value } 0.663 \quad \text{when } \frac{\bar{\sigma}}{\sigma_0} = 1.81$$

$$\longrightarrow \quad L_{max} \le 1.325 \frac{\bar{\sigma}}{q/A} \qquad\qquad v_0 = -0.448 \frac{\bar{\sigma}}{q/A_{cable}}$$

$\bar{\sigma} = \dfrac{\bar{N}}{A}$, allowable cable stress $(x = 0, x = L)$

Glossary

Adhesion: The state in which two surfaces are held together at an interface by forces or the interlocking action of an adhesive or both.

Advanced composites: Composite materials with structural properties comparable to or better than those of aluminium.

AFRP: Aramid-fibre reinforced plastic.

Aluminium (Al): Metallic element, melting point 660 degrees Celsius, density 2700 kg.m-3. Uses: ubiquitous aerospace alloy base.

Aramid: Polyparaphenylene terephthalamide, a type of highly oriented aromatic polymer material. Used primarily as a high-strength fibre. Available on the market as Kevlar and Twaron.

Autoclave: A closed vessel for conducting a chemical reaction or other operation under pressure and heat.

Bi-directional laminate: A reinforced plastic laminate with the fibres oriented in two directions.

Biomimetics: Design synthetic materials that function like natural ones. e.g. tendons.

Bond strength: The amount of adhesion between bonded surfaces; a measure of the stress required to separate a layer of material from the base to which it is bonded.

Braiding: A mechanical weaving of fibres into a structural form such as a tube, a square box or a U-shaped channel.

Buckling: Unstable displacement of a structural part, such as a panel, caused by excessive compression and/or shear. Microbuckling of fibres in a composite material can also occur under axial compression.

Butt Joint: The edge faces of the two parts are at right angles to their other faces.

Capsular wall: An organic, usually perforated wall, surrounding the central capsule of Radiolaria.

Carbon (C): Non-metallic element, melting point 3550 degrees Celsius, density 2200 kg.m-3. Uses: reinforcement fibres.

Carbon fibre: Fibre produced by the pyrolysis of organic precursor fibres, such as rayon, polyacrylonitrile, in an inert environment.

Ceramic: Chemical compound or mixture of compounds with high temperature capabilities, often metal (or silicon) oxides, nitrides or carbides.

Ceramic matrix composite: Composite material in which the matrix is a ceramic.

Cortical shell: An outermost shell enclosing one or more concentrically located inner shells.

CFRP: Carbon-fibre reinforced plastic.

CFRTP: Carbon fibre reinforced thermoplastic.

Composite (material): Material that is made of two or more constituent materials.

Crack: An actual separation of moulding material visible on opposite surfaces of the part and extending through the thickness.

Creep: The change in dimension of a material, under constant load over a period of time.

Cure: To change the properties of a resin by chemical reaction with or without pressure.

Curvature: Geometric measure of the bending and twisting of a plate.

Cytoplasm: The proteins of which cell matter consists.

Deformation: Changes in size and shape of a body resulting from externally applied stresses, temperature change, and moisture absorption.

Delamination: Physical separation or loss of bond of the layers of materials in a laminate.

Elastomer: Elastic substance occurring naturally as rubber, or produced synthetically as a specific gradation of many polymer materials.

Element: A generic part of a more complex structural member.

End: A strand of roving consisting of a given number of filaments gathered together.

Engineering constants: Measured directly from uniaxial tensile and compressive, and pure shear tests applied to unidirectional as well as laminated composites. Typical constants are the effective Young's modulus, Poisson's ratio, and shear modulus.

Epoxy resins: Thermosetting resins made by polymerization of epoxides or oxiranes with other materials such as amines, alcohols, phenols and unsaturated compounds.

Fabric: Planar, woven material constructed by interlacing yarns, fibres or filaments.

Fatigue: In materials or structures, the cumulative irreversible damage incurred by cyclic mechanical and/or thermal load in given environments. Fatigue can initiate and extend cracks.

Fibre: Single filament, rolled, formed in one direction, and used as the principal constituent of woven and non woven composite materials. Most common fibres are glass, boron, carbon and aramid.

Fibre surface treatment: Carbon fibres are usually given a postgraphitization surface treatment by either a chemical or an electro-mechanical method. The surface treatment enhances the bond between the fibres and the resin matrix in the cured laminate. This improves the shear and compressive properties of laminates.

Filament: A continuous discrete fibre. The cross-section is not necessarily circular.

Filament winding: Automated process of placing filament onto a mandrel in prescribed pattern. The resin impregnation can be before or during the winding, known as prepreg or wet winding. The mandrel can be removed after curing of the composite materials. Filament winding is most advantageous in building pressure vessels.

Geodesic: The shortest distance between two points on a curved surface.

Geodesic isotensoid: Constant-stress level in any given filament at all points in its path.

Geodesic isotensoid contour: In filament wound reinforced plastic pressure vessels, a dome contour in which the filaments are placed on geodesic paths so that under pressure loading the filaments will exhibit uniform tension throughout their length.

GFRP: Glass-fibre reinforced plastic.

Hand lay-up: The process of placing (and working) successive plies of reinforcing materials or resin-impregnated reinforcement in position on a mould by hand.

Honeycomb: Manufactured product of resin-impregnated sheet material (paper, glass fabric, etc.) or sheet metal formed into hexagonal-shaped cells; used as a core material in sandwich constructions.

Impact damage: A structural anomaly created by the impact of a foreign object.

Impregnate: In reinforced plastics, to saturate the reinforcement with a resin.

Iron (Fe): Metallic element, melting point 1538 degrees Celsius, density 7870 kg.m-3. Uses: base element for steels, iron-based alloys, alloying additions.

Isotropy: Property that is not directionally dependent (having the same physical and/or mechanical properties in all material directions). Metals are often assumed to be isotropic. This is normally not the case, but they do generally show considerably more isotropy than fibre-reinforced composites.

Joint: The location at which two different parts are held together. It is the general area of contact for a bonded structure.

Laminate: Plate consisting of layers of uni- or multidirectional plies of one or more composite materials.

Lap Joint: A joint made by placing one element partly over another and bonding together the overlapped portions.

Microtubule: A slender intracellular tube composed of protein and forming a cytoskeletal framework within a cell.

Modulus: An elastic constant defined as the ratio between the applied stresses and the related deformation, such as Young's modulus, shear modulus, or stiffness moduli in general.

Mould: The cavity or matrix in or on which the plastic, metal or ceramic composition is placed and from which it takes its form.

Multifilament yarn: A multitude of fine, continuous filaments (often 5 to 100), usually with some twist in them to facilitate handling.

Peel strength: Bond strength, obtained by peeling the layer.

Plastic: A material that contains as an essential ingredient an organic substance of high molecular weight, is solid in its finished state, and at some stage in its processing into finished articles can be shaped by flow.

Polyester: Thermosetting resin produced by dissolving unsaturated, generally linear alkyd resins in a vinyl active monomer, for instance styrene, or methyl styrene.

Polymer: A high-molecular-weight organic compound, natural or synthetic, whose structure can be represented by a repeated small unit, e.g. polyethylene, etc.. Synthetic polymers are formed by addition or condensation polymerization of monomers. Some polymers are elastomers, some plastics.

Porosity: Voids remaining in a material or component after manufacture, e.g. gas bubbles in fibre reinforced resin products, gas or vacuum voids in metal castings. The porosity of a material is normally expressed as the ratio of the volume of air or void contained within the boundaries of a material to the total volume.

Prepreg: Short for pre-impregnated

Pyrolysis: The subjection of an organic compound to very high temperatures.

Reinforced plastic: A plastic with strength properties greatly superior to those of the base resin.

Reinforcement: A strong inert material bonded into a plastic, metal or ceramic to improve its strength, stiffness and impact resistance. Reinforcements are usually long fibres in woven or non woven form. To be effective, the reinforcing material must form a strong adhesive bond with the matrix.

Resin: A solid, semi-solid, or pseudo-solid organic material which has an indefinite (often high) molecular weight, exhibits a tendency to flow when subjected to stress, usually has a softening or melting range, and usually fractures conchoidally. Most resins are polymers.

Roving: Loose assemblage of filaments with no twist. Roving can be impregnated for use in filament winding, braiding, and in unidirectional tapes.

Safety factor: The ratio of the ultimate design loads to the limit of applied loads.

Scarf Joint: A joint made by cutting away similar angular segments of two parts and bonding them with the cut areas fitted together.

Shear stress: Stress component that results in distortion; other stress components result in extension or contraction.

Smart structure: A structure or mechanism with sensory and reactive elements which, when activated will monitor or modify the structure or mechanism characteristics.

Spray-up: Techniques with a spray gun as the processing tool. In reinforced plastics, fibres and resin can be simultaneously deposited in a mould. In essence, roving is fed through a chopper, ejected into a resin stream, and directed.

Stiffness: Ratio between the applied stress and the resulting strain. Young's modulus is the stiffness of a material subjected to uniaxial stress; shear modulus to shear stress. For composite materials, stiffness and other properties are dependent on the orientation of the material.

Strand: A bundle of continuous filaments combined in a single compact unit without twist.

Strength: Maximum stress that a material can sustain.

Stress: Intensity of forces within a body. The normal components induce length or volume change, the shear component, shape change.

Stress concentration: Increased ratio of local stress over the average stress.

Tape: Unidirectional prepreg of continuous length.

Thermoplastic: Organic material, the stiffness of which can be reversibly altered by temperature change.

Thermoset: Polymer that sets in a chemical reaction and cannot be remoulded.

Tintinnid: A marine ciliate typically forming a conical or trumpet-shaped lorica either formed by a secreted organic substance or by cementing small particles together.

Titanium (Ti): Metallic element, melting point 1670 degrees Celsius, density 4540 kg.m-3. Matrix alloy for composites, structural material for aerospace uses generally where operational temperatures exceed those possible with aluminium.

Unidirectional composite: A composite having parallel fibres.

Warp: The yarn running lengthwise in a woven fabric; a group of yarns in long lengths and approximately parallel, put on beams or warp reels for further textile processing, including weaving.

Weft: The transverse threads or fibres in a woven fabric; fibres running perpendicular to the warp.

Wrinkle: A surface imperfection in laminated plastics.

Young's modulus: The ratio of a simple stress, applied to a material, to the resulting strain parallel to the tension.

Index

acid 44, 157
acoustic 60, 64, 65
aerofoil 46
Africa 16, 120, 138
Airship 18,19, 21
Akashi 77,126
amino 44
anchor 76, 77, 154
Antoni 31, 38, 126
Arab 138
arch 31, 39, 117, 120-122, 126
archer 84, 86, 91
Arenas 122
Armenia 105
arrow 83, 85, 86
Ashby 12-14, 21, 24, 56
Asia 16
Assyrian 27, 156, 157
Astrofilm 154
Aztecs 95
B2 59, 60
Bakker 148
balloon 18, 153, 154
balsa 104
bamboo 23, 31, 71, 73, 91
bandits 16
Barcelona 31, 38, 39
barrel 154
basket 76, 77
Bedouins 139
Bee 52
Beech 59
beer 23, 27, 152, 154, 155
belvedere 139
bending 26, 40, 41, 57, 66, 70, 82, 120, 127
Bergman 85
Bernard 138
Bey 150
bicycle 91, 93, 100, 101
Bill 139, 142
binder 132
black 137, 138, 145
blimp 19
BMW 18
Bohr 25
bone 12, 25, 44, 56, 57, 86
boomerang 89-91
bottle 23, 152
bow 25, 73, 83-86, 91, 96, 97
Bragg 91
brain 45
Branson 153
brick 26, 33, 121, 126, 142, 143
bridge 25, 26, 47, 49, 76, 77, 97, 114-127
Brooklyn 123, 126
Brunel 120, 121, 126
Bubka 91
buckling 35, 39, 40, 70, 91, 133
Buckminster 27, 33, 34, 52

Buffalo 139, 142
Burroughs 92, 93
cable 76, 120, 121, 123, 126, 127, 145, 154
Caesar 117
Cambridge 49
caravanserai 17
Carilon 159
Carolyn 47
cascade 111
cast 117, 120
cat 66
catenary 126, 127
cathedral 38
Cayley 100
cellulose 27
ceramic 13, 25, 71, 73, 77
chair 59
chariot 85, 92, 96, 97
Charles 153
chasm 116
Cheetah 93
children 143
China 95, 97, 157
choice 110
Chrysler 40
cigar 132, 133
circle 50, 53, 76, 85, 86, 90, 143
Claudia 39
clay 12, 52, 73, 77
Clifton 126, 127
climate 34, 137, 145
Cody 139, 142
Cold 103, 104, 107
Comet 123, 126
concentration 61
concrete 31, 47, 68, 73, 77, 96, 121
cool 103
Corbusier 33
crack 40, 41, 52, 61
creep 91, 96, 97
crutches 39
cucumber 46
cushion 153
cytoplasm 49, 50
cytoskeleton 52
dagger 83
De Havilland 123
deck 120, 122, 126, 127
diamond 92, 135
disc 95, 100, 101
distaff 95, 129
dome 33, 35, 52
Domina 142
Douglas 13
draping 129, 131-133, 137, 142, 145
dresses 131
Droog 148
Dry 47, 148, 149
Durrani 142
Dymaxion 27, 33, 34

edge 73, 131
egg 23, 147
Egyptian 97
Eiffel 39, 121
elastic 60, 70, 78, 86, 121
EMPA 77
Eric 132
Euler 39, 40
exhaust 135
exoskeleton 46
Extra 58-61, 64, 66, 143
Faegre 138, 139
Familia 31, 38
fashion 129, 132
Feather 89, 103, 104, 107
felt 143, 148
Felix 89
fish 60
flowers 103
foam 56, 57, 60, 79, 106
Fokker 13
Formica 73
France 120, 156
Frei 30, 50, 143
Fuller 27, 33, 34, 52
Gaudí 31, 38-41, 126, 149
gel 46
Genghis 30, 137
Germany 59, 147
Gibraltar 120
Giffard 19
Gijs 148
giraffe 50, 52
girder 52, 77, 103, 106
goat 27, 138, 156
golf 89
Goodyear 19
Gordon 26, 27, 30, 31, 39, 40, 96,
100, 117, 120
gravity 49, 50
Grumman 59, 60
Güell 39, 40
Haeckel 50
Hafkamp 109
hair 12, 138
Hardy 83
helium 19, 153
Hell 122
helmet 133, 135
Hess 89
Hexacan 24
hexagon 33, 49, 50, 53, 56
Hindenburg 18
Hole 61
honeycomb 24, 52, 53, 56
Hoogendijk 149
horn 12, 25, 26, 73, 86
hunting 83, 84, 89
icecream 103
inflatable 27, 152, 153
Ingber 50, 52

iron 117, 120, 126, 127
Issey 132
Ishi 83, 84
iso-tensoid 153, 155
Jalbert 142
Japan 77, 126, 139, 147
John 83
joint 45, 73, 76, 97
Jongerius 148-150
Julian 43
Kahn 30, 137
Kaikyo 77, 126
Karakalpak 143
Kazakhs 143
Keegan 83, 86
khana 142, 143
kite 23, 138,139, 142
knitting 130, 150
Kobe 127
Konings 150
Kooi 85
Kublai 30
Lakehurst 18
lamp 150
lattice 143
leaf 132, 133
Liliënthal 24, 57, 96
limb 73, 84-86
loam 145
logistics 113, 156
longbow 83, 85
LPG 154, 156, 157, 159
Lur 142
M5 79, 150
macramé 149
matrix 70, 73, 79
meat 103, 106
Meier 120
Mercedes 11, 17, 18
Messina 122, 127
Michell 57
milk 27, 152, 156
Miyake 132
moist 49, 145
Mongols 142
monocoque 92, 93
Montgolfier 153
Moscow 101
mountain 116, 126, 139
mud 12, 31
Munich 138, 145
nanocomposite 77
nature 21, 24, 44-50, 56, 57, 110
New York 40, 122, 149
nomad 25, 116
Northrop 59, 60
oil 112, 143, 157
Otten 132, 133
Otto 30, 50, 57, 96, 143
Oud 33
Panamarenko 153

Pantaleon 122
parachute 154
paradigm 44, 47
payload 65, 103, 120, 122, 127
Pearce 49, 52
photochromic 44, 45
Piano 143
piezoëlectric 46
polevaulting 12, 91
poly-urethane 106, 107, 147, 150
Pope 94
pressurized 64
prestress 30
prototype 65, 104, 159
PVC 106, 150
Quadrax 73
racing 89, 92
Radiolaria 49, 50, 53, 65, 66
railroad 117
Ramakers 148
rebound 113
receptor 45
recurve 85
Renny 148
Renzo 143
Richard 33, 153
rituals 143
Robert 83, 120
robot 45, 46
Rocket 120
rope 96, 143
Rotterdam 110
Rozier 153
RTM 101
rubber 19, 76, 77, 89, 135, 147,
155, 159
Rudofsky 138
S-curve 12, 13, 59, 60, 85
Sagrada 31, 38
salmon 84
sandwich 57, 60, 61, 64, 66, 71, 103
sapwood 84
Schafer 18, 19
Schiffer 39
sensor 44, 46
service 111-113
shaman 21
shepherd 137
Shibam 145
shoes 131
shrapnel 133
Sidney 122
silica 49, 50
simulation 129
sinew 26, 73, 84
skeleton 45, 47, 49,50, 59, 66
smart 44-47, 95
spaceframe 50
Spain 85
spear 83
Spirit 59, 60

sport 89
Spumellaria 49, 50
Starship 59
stealth 59
Stephenson 120
straw 12, 52, 68, 71, 73
string 23, 41, 126
sugar 44
sustainable 110-113
swamp 71
sweater 150
swing 143
Tacoma 126
tailoring 60, 78
tank 152, 157
Taxus 85
tensegrity 27, 33-35, 50, 52, 68,
153, 154
testing 66, 159
Thames 120
Thonet 97
tobacco 132, 133
Tokyo 16
Torvald 138
tourist 153
tree 30, 39, 44, 66, 95, 96, 116
triangle 50
tribe 83, 137, 138, 153
trinity 22, 23, 61, 71, 78, 103, 147, 153
truck 103-105, 107, 135, 155, 156
Tutankhamon 91, 96, 97
twig 38
Victor 18, 19
Vincent 43
Virgin153
Vivienne 132
wagon 97, 103, 105, 116, 156
Wanders 149, 150
war 83, 86, 89
warp 130, 135
wattle-and-daub 12, 23, 73
weapon 83, 86, 89
weft 130, 135
Westwood 132
wetting 78, 100, 116
wheel 94-97, 100, 101, 104, 129,
154, 155
Wichita 34
winding 129, 132
Wim 109
worm 46
wrapper 132, 133
X-29 60
X-ray 49
yak 138
Yemen 145
yew 85
Young 40, 70, 121
yurt 142, 143
zeppelin 18, 21, 33, 154
Zhongyuan 157

Biblio-graphy

Anderson, R., Radiolaria, Springer Verlag, New York 1983

Ashby, M.F., Materials selection in mechanical design, Pergamon Press, Oxford 1992

Attenborough, D., Life on earth, Elsevier, Amsterdam 1989

Beljon, J.J., Zo doe je dat; Grondbeginselen van vormgeving, Wetenschappelijke Uitgeverij bv, Amsterdam 1976

Bergsma, O.K., Three Dimensional Simulation of Fabric; Draping - Development & Application, Delft University Press, Delft 1996

Besseling, J.F., Stijfheid en sterkte 2; toepassingen, Oosthoek, Scheltema & Holkema, Utrecht 1975

Beukers, A., van Tooren, M.J.L., 'Ontwerp-filosofie van de Extra 400 koolstofromp', De Constructeur 5, May 1995, pp. 46-53

Beukers, A., de Haan, P., Ultralight multipurpose trailers or containers, Conference on innovative control for intermodal transport, Amsterdam 1997

Beukers, A., 'Vezelversterkte materialen voor lichte constructies, een renaissance', De Constructeur 10, October 1997, pp. 48-54

Bini, G., Atlante dei pesci delle coste Italiane, Mondo Sommerso editrice, Rome 1967

Brauns, C.D., Löffier, L.G., Mru - Hill people on the border of Bangladesh, Birkhäuser Verlag, Basel 1990

Brown, L., Bridges, Todtri Production Ltd., New York 1996

Brüggemann, H.M., Kunststoffen 1986; Terugblik en Toekomst, Kunstof en Rubber Instituut TNO, Rotterdam 1986

Carmichael, P., Nomads, Collins and Brown Ltd., London 1991

Cianchi, M., Leonardo da Vinci's Machines, Becocci Editore, Florence 1988

Desroches-Noblecourt, Ch., Tutankhamen; Life and death of a pharaoh, The Connoisseur and Michael Joseph Ltd. London 1969

Dothior, J., Des Architectures de Terre; ou l'avenir d'une tradition millénaire, Centre Georges Pompidou, Paris 1982

Donk, M. van der, Gerwen, T. van, De wonderwereld van de insekten, A.W. Sijthoff, Alphen aan den Rijn 1981

Engel, F.M., So bewegen sich die Tiere, Südwest Verlag, Munich 1970

Faegre, T., Tents, Architecture of the Nomads, John Murray, London 1979

Farrand jr., J., Weather, Stewart, Tabori & Chang, New York 1990

Gibson, L.J., Ashby, M.F., Cellular Solids. Structure & Properties, Pergamon Press, Oxford 1988

Gloudemans, C., Volken en stammen, Amsterdam Boek, Amsterdam, 1975

Gordon, J.E., Structures; or why things don't fall down, Penguin Books Ltd.,

London 1991

Hardy, R., Longbow. A social and military history, Patrick Stephens Ltd. London 1995

Heinzerling, W., Trischler, H., Otto Lilienthal; Flugpionier, Ingenieur, Unternehmer, Bertelsmann Lexikon Verlag, Munich 1991

Hess, F., 'The aerodynamics of boomerangs', Scientific American, November 1968, pp. 124-136

Humphries, D.A., Composites, ASM International, Metals Park, Ohio 1987

Illing, R., Japanese Prints, E.P. Dutton, New York 1978

Ingber, D.E., 'The architecture of life', Scientific American, January 1998, pp.30-39

Jong, Th. de, Het wikkelen van drukvaten volgens de 'netting' theorie, rapport VTH 166, Technische Hogeschool Delft, Delft 1971

Kashima, S., Kitagawa, M., 'The longest suspension bridge', Scientific American, December 1997, pp. 60-65

Katz, S., Classic Plastics; From Bakelite to High-Tech, Thames and Hudson, London 1984

Keegan, J., A history of warfare, Pimlico, London 1993

Koiter, W.T., Stijfheid en sterkte 1. Grondslagen, Scheltema & Holkema nv, Haarlem 1972.

Kooi, B.W., Bergman, C.A., 'An approach to the study of ancient archery using mathematical modelling', Antiquity 71, February 1997, pp. 124-134

Kroonenberg, H.H. van den, Duurzaam ontwerpen, ECN, Petten 1994

Mackenzie, D., Green Design; Design for the Environment, Laurence King, London 1991

Maginnity, B., 'Extra 400', Flying, December 1997, pp. 62-66

McHale, J., R. Buckminster Fuller, Otto Maier Verlag, Ravensburg 1964

McNeil, W.H., 'The excentricity of wheels, or Eurasian transportation in historical perspective', The American Historical Review 92 (1987), pp. 1111-1126

McNeil, W.H., 'Human migration in historical perspective', Population and Development Review 10 (1984), pp. 1-18

Meier, U., 'Proposal for a carbon fibre reinforced composite bridge across the Strait of Gibraltar at its narrowest site', Proceedings from the Institution of Mechanical Engineers, Vol 201 B2 1987, pp. 184-189

Michaud, R. and S., Caravans to Tartary, Thames and Hudson, London 1978

Miller, M.E., The Art of Mesoamerica; from Olmec to Aztec, Thames and Hudson, London 1993

Miravete, A., 3-D textile reinforcements in composite materials, Woodhead Publishing Ltd., Cambridge 1998

Otto, F., Das hängende Dach, Deutsche Verlags-Anstalt, Stuttgart 1954

Pearce, P., Structure in nature is a strategy for design, MIT Press, Cambridge 1990

Pelham, D., Kites, Penguin Books Ltd., New York 1976

Picon, A., L'Art de l'ingénieur constructeur entrepreneur inventeur, Le Moniteur/Centre Georges Pompidou, Paris 1997

Pigott, S., The earliest wheeled transport; from the Atlantic coast to the Caspian Sea, Thames and Hudson, London 1983

Platt, C., The atlas of mediaeval man, St Martin's Press, New York 1979

Ramakers, R., Bakker, G., Droog Design, 010 Publishers, Rotterdam 1998

Reeves, N., Toetanchamon; De koning, het graf, de schatten, H.J.W. Becht, Haarlem 1991

Robroek, L.J.M., The development of rubber forming as a rapid thermoforming technique for continuous fibre reinforced thermoplastic composites, Delft University Press, Delft 1994

Roca, P., González, J.L., Mari,A.R., Oñate, E., Structural analysis of historical constructions; possibilities of numerical and experimental techniques, CIMNE, Barcelona 1997

Rosenbaum, A., Works in Progress, Pomegranate Artbooks, San Francisco 1994

Rudofsky, B., Architecture Without Architects, Academy Editions, London 1964

Rudofsky, B., The Prodigious Builders, Harvest/Harcourt Brace Jovanovich, New York 1977

Schafer, A., Victor, D., 'The past and future of global mobility', Scientific American, October 1997, pp. 36-39

Schatzberg, E., 'Ideology and technical choice: the decline of the wooden airplane in the United States, 1920-1945', Technology and Culture 35(1) (1994), pp. 34-69

Szabo, A., Barfield, Th.J., Afghanistan; An atlas of indigenous domestic architecture, University of Texas Press, Austin 1991

Tomlow, J., Das Modell; Antonio Gaudis Hängemodel und seine Rekonstruktion; neue Erkentnisse zum Entwurf, Karl Krämer Verlag, Stuttgart 1989

Tooren, M.J.L. van, Sandwich fuselage design, Delft University Press, Delft 1998

Wegener Sleeswijk, A., Wielen wagens koetsen, Hedeby Publishers, Leeuwarden 1993

Winter, S.E.E. de, Thermoplasten in de carosseriebouw CLC TUD-TNO 97300 SWR, University of Technology, Delft 1997

Woolley, L., History unearthed, Ernest Benn Ltd., London 1958

Zerbst, R., Antoni Gaudi í Cornet; ein Leben in Architektur, Benedikt

Taschen Verlag, Cologne 1988
Nationalgalerie Berlin, Panamarenko, Nationalgalerie Berlin 1978

Various authors, Twee miljoen jaren beschaving, Reader's Digest,
Amsterdam 1973

Various authors, Success through Friendship, F-27 Friendship Association,
F-27 Symposium, Amsterdam 1992

Various authors, Vijftig jaar 'Vliegtuigbouwkunde' in Delft 1940-1990, Delft
University Press, Delft 1990

Vicenty, W.G., What engineers know and how they know it; analytical studies from aeronautical history, The John Hopkins University Press, Baltimore
1990

Dutch summary

A bathtub full of change

Er is iets geks aan de hand met lichtheid van constructies, want voor het koffertje van een zakenman geldt het lage gewicht als een statussymbool, terwijl de veel te zware auto waarin hij zich laat rondrijden dat ook is. Toch is dat koffertje ook een teken dat lichtheid als belangrijke eigenschap onvermijdelijk steeds belangrijker gaat worden. Dat komt doordat alles wat met transport te maken heeft – en dat is heel veel, want het gaat zowel om vervoermiddelen als lading – enorme hoeveelheden energie verbruikt. En energie wordt schaars.

Er blijkt een parallel te zijn met de oudheid. Toen moest ook alles licht zijn, omdat mensen vanwege hun nomadisch bestaan alles zelf moesten kunnen dragen. Zij gebruikten spullen die vaak nog steeds als voorbeeld kunnen dienen voor hoe we nu dingen moeten maken. Composieten, bijvoorbeeld, zijn al duizenden jaren oud.

Dat valt allemaal af te leiden uit de 'badkuipkromme' van Ashby. De grafiek geeft het verloop aan in de verhouding tussen het gebruik van verschillende groepen materialen. We kunnen eruit afleiden dat metalen steeds meer in zwang raakten en dat zij zich rond de Tweede Wereldoorlog op hun hoogtepunt bevonden. Er is niet veel fantasie voor nodig om het verband met lichtheid te begrijpen. Vanaf het midden van de twintigste eeuw beginnen kunststoffen en moderne composieten op te komen.

Het belang van lichtheid hangt ook samen met onze vervoersbehoefte. Onderzoek laat zien dat op dat gebied onverwachte constante factoren gelden. Zo bedraagt de factor transport bij een product altijd grofweg drie procent van de totale kosten, ongeacht of het per kameel of per vliegtuig gebeurt. Verder besteedt iedereen over de hele wereld gemiddeld ongeveer evenveel tijd aan vervoer: één tot anderhalf uur per dag. Het verschil schuilt in de afstand en de snelheid waarmee wordt gereisd. In de VS neemt vanwege de snelheid het aandeel van auto's al af ten opzichte van dat van de luchtvaart.

Metalen, vooral aluminium en staal, zijn op hun retour. Ze zijn zogezegd aan de top van hun S-curve, de grafiek die het verband aangeeft tussen verhoging van hun prestaties en de moeite die je daarvoor moet doen. Een bescheiden verbetering van een metaaltechnologie kost nu naar verhouding veel tijd en geld. Onder zulke omstandigheden is het verstandig de sprong te maken naar een hele andere technologie met de veel lichtere composietmaterialen.

The trinity essence

Lichtheid is niet alleen een kwestie van materiaalkeuze. Er is altijd een samenhang tussen vorm, materiaal en vervaardigingsproces. Blikjes kun je bijvoorbeeld lichter maken door de wand van een honingraatstructuur te voorzien. Vorm, materiaal en maakproces vormen een drie-eenheid. Het ligt voor de hand dat de balans tussen de drie elementen kritieker wordt, naarmate de constructie minder mag wegen.

Constructies moeten daarom efficiënt zijn. Om te beginnen betekent dit, dat ze zo min mogelijk gebukt moeten gaan onder hun eigen gewicht, want dat is verspilde energie. Bruggen hebben een maximale overspanning die afhangt van hun zwaarte.

Verder hangt efficiëntie af van het soort belasting dat de constructie moet kunnen opnemen. Dan is buiging in het algemeen ongunstig, omdat ze zelf tot zowel druk in de wand als trek in de buitenbocht, als trek in de buitenbocht. Weinig materialen zijn goed in het opvangen van allebei. Hout kan niet zo goed tegen druk en steen niet tegen trek. Daarom is het verstandig het materiaal aan te passen aan het soort belasting. Duizenden jaren geleden waren de makers van composiet handbogen voor jacht en strijd daarvan al op de hoogte. De kern van zo'n boog was van hout, de buitenbocht van pees, ideaal voor trek en de binnenbocht van hoorn, dat goed tegen druk kan.

Het opvangen van trekbelasting heeft het voordeel ten opzichte van druk dat er minder materiaal voor nodig is. Trek leidt tot rank en dun. Met kabels en stangen en met membraan of doek (tent, ballon) zijn goede constructies te maken, mits de trek wordt gecompenseerd door dikkere op druk belaste elementen. Zuivere druk kan worden opgevangen met de boogvorm.

Tensegrity hero

De grote meester van het verkennen van construeren op trek was de Amerikaan Buckminster Fuller. Hij was geïnspireerd door zeilschepen en bedacht vederlichte woningen die per zeppelin naar hun locatie konden worden overgebracht, met inrichting en al. Ook ontwikkelde hij een eigen jargon met termen als 'tensegrity', een samentrekking van tension en integrity. De essentie van een tensegrity-constructie is, dat alle trekbelasting wordt opgenomen door een enkel continu element, bijvoorbeeld een kabel, terwijl afzonderlijke korte dikke elementen de drukkrachten voor hun rekening nemen.

Compression champion

Ranke constructies die toch gebaseerd waren op het opvangen van drukbelasting waren de specialiteit van Antoni Gaudí. Hij ontwikkelde een geheel eigen methode om de vorm te bepalen van de bogen die zijn gebouwen ondersteunden. Daartoe maakte hij de structuur eerst ondersteboven, met touwtjes en gewichtjes. De zwaartekracht zorgde dat de hangende constructie de optimale vorm aannam. Het enige wat de metselaars hoefden te doen was de vorm omgekeerd na te bouwen.

Toch klopte de redenering van de Catalaanse architect niet helemaal. Er zijn scheurtjes ontdekt in de crypte die hij bouwde in de arbeiderskolonie Güell. Er werken meer krachten op een gebouw dan alleen de zwaartekracht. Bovendien kun je de dunne op trek belaste touwtjes niet straffeloos omzetten in dik metselwerk, want dikte introduceert de kans op buigbelasting en daar kan steen niet goed tegen. Ranke constructies onder druk lopen ook kans te bezwijken door knik, het gevolg van instabiliteit.

Smart by nature

Wie niet sterk is moet slim zijn. Minimaliseren van de hoeveelheid benodigd materiaal kan ook door te denken in termen van slimme ('smart') concepten. Ze werken met sensoren, een 'denkende' rekeneenheid, en actuatoren. Julian Vincent vergelijkt een klassieke productierobot met een mens. De robot kan alleen gestructureerde, geprogrammeerde bewegingen maken en is daarom veel zwaarder geconstrueerd dan de flexibele mens in elkaar zit. Een mens weet waar zijn hand zich bevindt, maar een robot heeft daarvan geen benul.

Het waarnemen, denken en handelen kan ook op materiaalniveau plaatsvinden. Dan kom je uit bij slimme materialen. Het Engelse leger ontwikkelt een veranderbare aerofoil, waarvan de huid gebaseerd is op die van de zeekomkommer. Hij kan stijver en slapper worden. Dat gebeurt op basis van het voorbeeld van de wurm. Daarin zit een gel die geprikkeld kan worden tot het opnemen of afstaan van vocht. Het is verbazingwekkend hoeveel kracht je kunt uitoefenen met de volumeverandering die daarvan het gevolg is. Denk maar aan een slappe plant die overeind komt als je hem water geeft. Je kunt zelfs materialen die zich leren aanpassen aan omstandigheden.

Nature as a rolemodel

De natuur levert talrijke voorbeelden van structuren die met minimale hoeveelheden materiaal een maximale hoeveelheid energie kunnen opvangen. Haar luiheid heeft algemene principes opgeleverd. De driehoek is zo'n grondbeginsel. Zet drie latjes met de uiteinden aan elkaar en de zaak is volkomen stijf. Een herhaling van driehoeken levert een spaceframe op. De middelpunten van drie even grote bollen liggen elkaar vormen samen ook een driehoek en zes bollen rondom net zo'n bol in het midden definiëren een zeshoek.

Dat is een vorm die je overal tegenkomt waar energie geminimaliseerd moet worden: droge klei, basalt, de honingraat, noem maar op. Een vlak dat is verdeeld in driehoeken hoeft niet plat te zijn. Radiolaria zijn fascinerende micro-organismen met prachtige uitwendige glazen skeletjes, waarvan het ontstaan van een zeshoekige onderverdeling duidelijk is af te lezen. De echte ruimtelijke pendant van de zeshoek ontstaat bij het stapelen van bollen. Als zij wanden met elkaar delen, zoals in zeepsop te zien is, dan blijkt dat het veertienvlak een ideale krachtenverdeling op te leveren. En dat is dan ook precies wat je ziet in schuim. Ook dat is een veel voorkomende lichte structuur. Het is te vinden in bot. Een doorgezaagde kop van een menselijk dijbeen geeft aan dat de schuimstructuur zich zo heeft gevormd dat krachten optimaal worden doorgeleid, zodat de materiaalspanningen niet te hoog oplopen. In Delft in het Laboratorium voor Structuren en Materialen is een methode ontwikkeld om schuim te maken met een schoon blaasmiddel. Minimale energieverspilling is zelfs terug te vinden op het niveau van het eiwitskelet van cellen. Het blijkt dat dit kan worden verklaard met het tensegrity-principe dat Buckminster Fuller voor het eerst bewust heeft toegepast.

Extra 400

Voor de vliegtuigbouw heeft oorspronkelijk de vogel als voorbeeld gediend. Door de overwinning van de metaaltechnologie tussen de twee wereldoorlogen en door specialisatie is het ideaalbeeld enigszins op de achtergrond geraakt, maar onder meer dankzij composieten doemt het weer op. Vooral in de militaire luchtvaart en de zakenwereld zijn de composieten sterk in opkomst. Het eerste volledig van kunststof vervaardigde vliegtuig was de Starship van Beech, een bedrijf dat vanouds voorop loopt met ontwikkelingen. De Spirit B2 Stealth bommenwerper van Northrop heeft dan wel veel weg van een vogel, toch is zijn vorm al veel vanzelfsprekender dan die van zijn voorgangers. Verkeersvliegtuigen ijlen na. Voor een deel komt dat doordat er meer productie-ontwikkeling nodig is.

Het construeren met composieten is eenvoudiger dan met metaal. Er zijn minder onderdelen door de integratie van functies, zoals de mechanische eigenschappen, akoestische demping en thermische isolatie in een enkel materiaal: composiet sandwichplaat. Dat heeft als bijkomend voordeel dat gaten in een cilinderwand van dat materiaal, bijvoorbeeld voor de raampjes, veel minder problematisch zijn. Het Laboratorium heeft daarvan dankbaar gebruik gemaakt bij de ontwikkeling van de Extra 400, een klein zakenvliegtuigje dat nu in Duitsland wordt geproduceerd.

Het heeft een drukkajuit om op grote hoogte te kunnen vliegen. Verkeersvliegtuigen hebben dat ook, maar hun metalen constructie is niet ideaal. De huid zit namelijk aan de buitenkant op de spanten geklonken om de luchtweerstand minimaal te houden. De Extra 400 daarentegen, heeft een uitwendig skelet, net als Radiolaria. De overdruk in de cabine drukt de wand vanzelf tegen de binnenkant van de spanten aan. Met composieten hoeft de gladheid van de buitenkant van de romp daar niet onder te lijden.

Win-win materials

Er zijn grofweg vijf groepen materialen: metalen, kunststoffen, keramische materialen, hernieuwbare materialen (alles wat groeit) en koolstof. Composieten zijn combinaties van materialen uit meestal twee verschillende groepen die samen meer presteren dan afzonderlijk. Zelfs gewapend beton is op te vatten als een composiet van een keramisch materiaal en ijzer. Niettemin is het de gewoonte composieten op te vatten als een combinatie van een kunststof met wat anders. Er zijn twee groepen kunststoffen. De thermoharders krijgen hun definitieve vorm in een chemische reactie. Daarna zijn ze niet meer te vervormen. Thermoplasten worden zacht bij verhitting en kunnen meer dan eens worden vervormd.

Kunststoffen laten zich met van alles en nog wat tot composieten verbouwen: glasdeeltjes, klei, jute, kwarts. Voor lichte, sterke en stijve constructies komen de kunststoffen die zijn verstevigd met continue vezels het eerst in aanmerking. De meest bekende sterke vezels zijn glas, aramide en koolstof. Deze kunnen op verschillende manieren worden verwerkt.

De vezels kunnen parallel liggen (unidirectioneel), of de vorm van weefsel hebben. Vezels en weefsels kunnen verder in een mal worden aangebracht, waarna het impregneren met kunststof plaatsvindt, zoals bij RTM (Resin Transfer Moulding), of ze kunnen van tevoren worden geïmpregneerd. Dan ontstaan de zogeheten prepregs, die in of op de mal tot eindproduct worden verwerkt. Natuurlijk kunnen ook verschillende lagen op elkaar worden aangebracht: lamineren. Dat geeft een extra voordeel, want door het manipuleren

van de onderlinge oriëntatie van de vezels in de verschillende lagen beheerst de ontwerper het elastische gedrag van het materiaal: 'elastic tailoring'. De methode is bruikbaar om vervorming functionele kwaliteit te geven. Het lastige van composieten is de afwerking van uiteinden en randen. Kabelbruggen met koolstofkabels zijn vooral moeilijk te maken doordat er nog niet veel goede oplossingen bestaan voor de verankering. Koolstof is veel brosser dan staal.

Dat composieten ondanks hun veelbelovende eigenschappen moeite hebben een plek te veroveren in de vliegtuigindustrie komt vooral doordat vliegtuigbouw zelf nog nauwelijks bestond toen de metalen opkwamen. Nu is het een branche met een metaaltraditie die niet makkelijk te doorbreken is.

Bending for power

Composieten bestaan al heel lang en waren ook in de oudheid al ongelooflijk geavanceerd. Ze werden onder meer gebruikt in de pijl en boog. Dat was tot de opkomst van vuurwapens een machtig wapen. Het bestreek honderden meters. Naar alle waarschijnlijkheid ontstond de boog ongeveer 10.000 jaar geleden. Hij wordt beschouwd als de eerste machine, omdat je er energie in kunt opslaan.

De eerste bogen waren van hout. Het duurde duizenden jaren voordat de composiet boog ontstond, want dat was niet zomaar een uitvindinkje. Het is een gelamineerde constructie. Het maken ervan kost veel tijd. De Turkse composietboog bestaat uit vijf stukken hout die aan elkaar worden gelijmd. Het geheel wordt onder verhitting gekromd, waarna aan de ene kant, de uiteindelijke voorkant, peesweefsel wordt gelijmd en aan de andere kant hoorn. Het opspannen gebeurt tegen de kromming in, dus bocht die in ontspannen toestand bol is, wordt uiteindelijk hol. Daardoor ontstaat een behoorlijke voorspanning. De kracht die nodig is om zo'n boog te spannen kan 60 tot 70 kilo bedragen.

De vorm van een composiet boog wordt gekenmerkt door een 'recurve', een tegenbocht in de uiteinden. De minder machtige houten 'longbow', het wapen van Robin Hood, heeft dat niet. Afgezien van het vermogen heeft de composietboog het voordeel dat ruiters te paard hem kunnen gebruiken. Ook Indianen kennen de composietboog.

Fake warfare

Boogschieten is nu een sport, maar sport is wel één van de menselijke activiteiten die tot technische innovatie uitnodigen. Eigenlijk is dat vreemd, want sport is een krachtmeting in iets moeilijks terwijl de ontwikkelingen er steeds op zijn gericht dat moeilijke makkelijker te maken. Dat zal ermee te maken hebben dat sport oorspronkelijk oefening voor de jacht en het gevecht was.

Regels spelen een belangrijke rol in sportieve innovatie. Sommige veranderingen mogen gewoon niet. Een honkbalknuppel moet van hout zijn en wielrennen op een ligfiets is niet toegestaan. De polsstok voor het hoogspringen is niet zo aan regels gebonden en is dan ook regelmatig verbeterd. In het begin was hij van bamboe, later van aluminium. In 1961 werd voor het eerst een wereldrecord neergezet met een stok van glasfiber. De grote meester Sergei Bubka's stok is versterkt met glas- en koolstofvezels.

Ook de fiets is, vooral de laatste jaren, aan verlichting onderhevig. Het monocoque frame van koolstofcomposiet – het is bijzonder licht en stijf – is sterk in opkomst, vooral sinds in 1996 de Lotusfiets, ontworpen door Mike Burrows, zeer overtuigend won op de Olympische spelen. Onlangs is de eerste stadsfiets van koolstofcomposiet op de markt verschenen, van dezelfde ontwerper.

Reinventing the wheel

Het gebruik van wielen is niet alleen een kwestie van uitvinden, maar ook van behoefte. Het is bekend dat de Azteken geen wagens hadden. Toch kenden ze het wiel, tenminste dat blijkt uit opgegraven speelgoed. De wielen daarvan waren afgeleid van de klos die wordt gebruikt voor het spinnen van beestenhaar. Ze hadden gewoon niet zoveel aan wagens, omdat ze in bergachtige streken woonden en geen trekdieren hadden.

In de vlakkere gebieden van Eurazië en Afrika lag dat wel even anders. Daar ontwikkelde het wiel zich van de schijf met een gat erin, niet veel meer dan een dikke plak hout, tot een geavanceerde constructie met spaken. Vooral de uiterst lichte strijdwagen, waarmee grote gebieden werden bestreken en dus veroverd, zorgde voor verspreiding van het idee.

De zes strijdwagens van Toetankhamon zitten buitengewoon geraffineerd in elkaar. De bovenbouw komt in vervaardigingstechniek overeen met de Thonetstoel uit de vorige eeuw, een van de eerste industrieel gemaakte meubelen. De wielen waren van composietmateriaal. Ze waren zo in elkaar gelijmd, dat de velgen onder voorspanning stonden. Men heeft zich vaak afgevraagd, waarom ze in het koningsgraf niet onder de wagen zaten, maar ernaast tegen de muur lagen. Het antwoord is de zogeheten 'kruip', het verschijnsel dat materialen die lang achter elkaar constant worden belast geleidelijk vervormen. Om die reden was het in die tijd gebruikelijk om wielen te ontlasten als ze niet werden gebruikt.

Spaken dienden aanvankelijk voor het opvangen van drukbelasting. Bijna een eeuw voordat een vliegtuig echt kon vliegen ontwikkelde Sir George Cayley een licht wiel met veel dunnere spaken die op trek kunnen worden belast. De naaf hangt eraan, in plaats van dat hij erop leunt. Zijn idee was bedoeld om vliegtuigen lichte wielen te geven, die sterk genoeg waren om op te landen. Tegenwoordig zijn verreweg de meeste fietswielen op dit idee gebaseerd. Daarin komt nu verandering. Het schijfwiel is terug, maar dan van met koolstofvezels versterkt composiet. Er wordt zelfs gewerkt aan wielen waarvan de banden van hetzelfde materiaal zijn als de rest, alleen veerkrachtiger.

Trailer gains payload

Het concept van de huidige trailer verschilt nauwelijks van dat van wagens uit de oudheid. De wielen zijn bevestigd aan chassisbalken. Het enige essentiële verschil is dat ossen zijn vervangen door een cabine met een motor. Als regel van de Europese overheid heeft gezorgd dat er nu een nieuw concept is, waarvoor de ideeën geleverd zijn door het Laboratorium voor Structuren en Materialen. Die regel luidt dat een geladen truck met oplegger niet zwaarder mag zijn dan 40 ton. De consequentie is dat zo'n trailer meer lading kan meenemen naarmate zijn eigen gewicht lager is.

De 'Cold Feather' is bedoeld voor geconditioneerd transport. Het bijzondere ervan is, dat hij geen chassisbalken heeft. De carrosserie is een zelfdragende constructie van sandwichpanelen met PVC schuim, en een huid van met aramidevezels versterkte epoxyhars. In de wanden zijn op strategische plaatsen integraal spanten van met koolstofvezels versterkte kunststof verwerkt. De trailer is drie ton lichter dan zijn stalen voorganger. Naar schatting is de terugverdientijd vier jaar. De extra winst bedraagt ongeveer 6000 gulden per jaar.

Lightweight economics

Economie houdt zich in het geheel niet bezig met lichtheid. Op zich is dat niet helemaal vreemd. Want economie gaat niet over fysica, maar over het maken van keuzes. Niettemin zit er wel degelijk een fysische dimensie aan deze wetenschap, omdat het resultaat van bijvoorbeeld een staalfabriek wordt gemeten in tonnen. Zelfs de milieu-econoom denkt niet in termen van lichtheid. En dat is wel degelijk eigenaardig, omdat deze discipline zich richt op het onderzoeken van fysische implicaties van economische activiteit: vervuiling, uitputting van natuurlijke hulpbronnen, enzovoort.

De nota 'Milieu en economie' schetst een perspectief van duurzame economische ontwikkeling. Met bestaande en nieuwe combinaties van producten en diensten kan in de hoogwaardige behoeften van de consument worden voorzien. Voor duurzame ontwikkeling is de groei even groot als de toename van de fysieke belasting van hulpbronnen en energie, terwijl de productie van afval en vervuiling daalt.

Om dat doel te kunnen bereiken moet aan de behoeften worden voldaan met innovatieve producten en diensten die het milieu ontzien. Tegen deze achter-

grond is het gebruik van lichte materialen en structuren cruciaal, omdat daarmee de functie verbetert, terwijl de milieubelasting afneemt. Dat strookt ook met het idee van dematerialisatie, waarbij de toegevoegde waarde toeneemt, terwijl datgene waaraan waarde wordt toegevoegd juist minder wordt. Het enige nadeel van composieten, dat overigens geen onoplosbaar probleem hoeft te zijn, is in dit verband dat ze moeilijk te recyclen zijn. Er schuilt ook een belofte in deze materialen. Het zijn in zekere zin brandstoffen. Het is geen gek idee om meer toegevoegde waarde uit fossiele brandstoffen te halen door ze eerst voor materialen te gebruiken en daarna pas voor het opwekken van energie.

Bridging the gap

De houten bruggen van weleer zullen een enkele keer op die manier aan hun eind gekomen zijn. Bruggen zijn voor de mens het middel bij uitstek om het landschap aan te passen aan zijn transportbehoefte. Van bruggen kun je altijd duidelijk aflezen hoe ze in elkaar zitten. Er heeft vooral de laatste anderhalve eeuw een duidelijke verschuiving plaatsgevonden van druk- naar trekbelasting. Dat hangt rechtstreeks samen met de gewenste overspanning.

De werking van stenen boogbruggen is volledig gebaseerd op drukbelasting. Door de vorm van de boog drukken alle stenen op elkaar, zonder dat ze kunnen wijken. Boogbruggen zijn het betrouwbaarst als de boog ongeveer half zo hoog is als breed. De beroemde bruggenbouwer Brunell spotte met dat uitgangspunt door een hele vlakke brug te bouwen. De stenen boogbrug overspant maximaal ongeveer 60 meter per boog.

Terwijle van de prijs werd steen in de vorige eeuw opgevolgd door gietijzer, dat ook heel goed op druk kan worden belast. Om de noodzaak tot klimmen – vooral lastig voor treinen – te beperken, kwamen er ook bruggen waarbij het dek tussen de bogen zat, in plaats van erboven.

Hangbruggen bestonden toen al lang in de vorm van eenvoudige touwconstructies. Zij moeten bruggenbouwers hebben geïnspireerd tot de kettingbrug, waarbij het dek is opgehangen aan een sterk uitvergrote fietsketting. Maar de uitvinding van staalkabel betekende een echte doorbraak. De overspanning nam toe tot ruim een kilometer. In Japan is onlangs een hele grote hangbrug gebouwd die zelfs meer dan twee kilometer haalt.

Voor bruggen van staalkabel is daarmee ongeveer de grens bereikt. Langere lopen het risico te bezwijken onder hun eigen gewicht. Dat wil niet zeggen dat er nooit grotere overspanningen zullen worden gehaald. Er bestaan al kleine bruggen van composietmateriaal, met kabels van koolstof. In theorie moet daarmee een overspanning van meer dan tien kilometer haalbaar zijn.

Frozen fabrics

Weefsels vormen de tweedimensionale pendant van kabels en touwen. Deze bestaan op hun beurt uit vezels, die de afgelopen dertig jaar een geweldige ontwikkeling hebben doorgemaakt. Een composiet bestaat uit een weefsel van vezels dat in zijn vorm is bevroren met behulp van een kunststof. Dat weefsel kan een holte omsluiten. Zo'n vorm maak je door wikkelen of vlechten. Dat textiel de basis is van veel composieten, betekent ook dat alle vormen van textiel in principe bruikbaar zijn. Er bestaan verschillende soorten weefsel. Breien, dat een veel beter vervormbaar doek oplevert, kan ook. Het is daarnaast mogelijk driedimensionale weefsels te maken. Daarmee is nog niet veel ervaring opgedaan.

Dat composieten voor een deel uit textiel bestaan betekent dat ze zich net als textiel kunnen laten behandelen. Ze zijn te draperen. Op dat gebied zouden technici veel kunnen leren van couturiers. De kunststof kan thermohardend zijn of thermoplastisch. Met laatstgenoemde is het schoner werken, omdat de noodzakelijke chemische reactie aan het vormen voorafgaat. Het manipuleren van textiel is lastig voor machines. Dat is één van de redenen dat composieten zo'n moeite hebben met metaal te concurreren.

In het Laboratorium voor Structuren en Materialen vindt op dat gebied veel ontwikkeling plaats. Zo wordt er gewerkt aan computerprogramma's om het draperen te simuleren, zodat het proces beter beheersbaar wordt.

Natuurlijk kunnen ook meer lagen composiet over elkaar heen worden gedrapeerd. In de nieuwe helm van het Nederlandse leger zijn het zelfs twintig lagen. Dat levert een hoofdbescherming op die iets lichter is dan een stalen helm, maar die veel betere bescherming biedt tegen impact.
Een heel ander idee is het wikkelen van band, een probleem dat in eerste instantie werd aangekaart door een student die het ontwerpen van nieuwe modellen sigaren wilde versnellen. Het is niet uitgesloten dat het bouwen van de romp van een vliegtuig in de toekomst overeenkomsten zal vertonen met het rollen van een sigaar.

Flimsy buildings

De wereld kent een enorme verscheidenheid aan verplaatsbare onderkomens. Er zijn grofweg twee soorten. Het lichtst zijn de gespannen tenten, waarbij een weefsel over stokken heen wordt gespannen. Deze tentstructuur inspireert veel architecten. Frei Otto is een van de meest uitgesproken tentliefhebbers. Toch maken maar weinig van zijn gebouwen echt gerbuik van de kwaliteiten van textiel.
De gedrapeerde tenten zijn wat zwaarder. Er wordt minder mee gereisd. Ze bestaan uit een tamelijk uitgebreid frame, waar lagen doek omheen worden gelegd. De zwarte tent is het meest wijd verbreid: van Noord-Afrika tot het oosten van Tibet. Het zwarte doek bestaat meestal grotendeels uit geitenhaar. De donkere kleur en de grofheid van het zwarte weefsel zorgen samen voor koelte in de woestijn. Er bestaan allerlei varianten. In hete droge omstandigheden is een vrijwel horizontaal dak praktisch, terwijl regen beter wordt verwerkt door het dak schuin te spannen. Klimaatbeheersing kan meestal worden bereikt door intelligente materiaaltoepassing. De dikke lemen muren van eeuwenoude woontorens in Yemen nemen 's nachts vocht op dat ze overdag weer afstaan. Zo ontstaat natuurlijke koeling.
De gedrapeerde tent is van oorsprong primitiever, maar hij heeft zich bij de Mongolen ontwikkeld tot een hoogwaardig woningtype: de yurt. Zo'n tent bestaat uit een aantal scharende hekwerken – tegenwoordig geproduceerd door bedrijfjes – die in een cirkel aan elkaar worden gezet, onderbroken door één deursponning. Op dat houten wandje komt een eenvoudig dakframe. Het geheel wordt bij elkaar gehouden door een brede band, die de trekkrachten opneemt. Gedrapeerde lagen vilt maken de yurt bijzonder weerbestendig. Zelfs de vlieger is op te vatten als een gebouw. Hij wordt namelijk vanouds onder meer gebruikt als verplaatsbare uitkijkpost. Vlak voor de opkomst van het vliegtuig had het Engelse leger nog een aantal van zulke vliegers in gebruik. Sinds 1963 bestaan er aerofoils, vliegers en parachutes die hun vorm ontlenen aan de luchtstroming. Ze hebben geen frame nodig.

Exploring expression

Lichtheid is niet de belangrijkste interesse van de ontwerpers die deelnamen aan het Dry-Tech project van Droog Design, een stichting die tot doel heeft ontwerpen te presenteren die de discussie over vormgeving moet aanwakkeren. Het gaat hun om materiaaluitdrukking en onbevangen ambachtelijke verkenning. Ondersteund door het Laboratorium voor Structuren en Materialen gingen ze met vezelversterkte kunststoffen aan de slag.
Het project leverde een zestal interessante ontwerpen op. De ontwerpers waren vooral gefascineerd door het feit dat dezelfde kunststof zowel hard als veerkrachtig kan zijn. De gewikkelde krukjes – glasvezel en M5, een nieuwe supervezel – zijn veerkrachtig van buiten en stijf van binnen. De 'Wave', een ligmat van vilt met polyurethaan heeft een wat stijvere steunrol.
De geknoopte stoel van Marcel Wanders kreeg de meeste aandacht. Hij bestaat uit een structuur die is gemacraméed van een veter uit koolstof- en aramidevezels. Het geheel is geïmpregneerd met epoxyhars, net als Gaudi's gebouwen opgehangen voor de vorm en vervolgens uitgehard.

Fill her up please

Het enige dat echt nodig is om vloeistoffen of gassen te omsluiten is een dun vlies. Toch is de gewoonte onstaan om ze in zware metalen tanks te transporteren. Om de efficiëntie van transport op te voeren wordt in Delft gewerkt aan de ontwikkeling van lichte tanks van composietmateriaal. De vorm die zich daarvoor het best leent, is gebaseerd op de isotensoïde, een lijn van gelijke trekspanning. Daarmee ontstaan tweedimensionale tensegrity structuren in de vorm van bollen of kazen. De ballon is een goed voorbeeld.
De verpakking van bier in zulke tanks is een veelbelovend project, aangezien de ARBO-wetgeving een maximaal hefgewicht voorschrijft dat door de nu gangbare metalen fusten wordt overschreden. Zo'n vat moet aan ingewikkelde chemische eisen voldoen. Zuurstof mag niet in contact komen met het bier, want daarvan wordt het bitter. Omgekeerd moet het koolzuur binnen worden gehouden. De nieuwe tank krijgt daarom twee huiden. De binnenste zorgt voor de chemische afscheiding en de buitenste vangt de trekspanning op. Voor het opbouwen van druk zijn geen gasflessen meer nodig. Een compressor volstaat. Er komt ook een consumentenversie. Het is een wegwerpverpakking die op de waterleiding kan worden aangesloten voor het opbouwen van druk om te tappen. De inhoud van een krat past in een licht bescheiden bolletje.
De kunststof LPG-tank is niet flexibel. Hij past in het compartiment voor het reservewiel. Ook deze bestaat uit meer lagen. De binnenhuid is van Carilon. Deze wordt omwikkeld met koolstofvezels. Ter bescherming wordt daaromheen een laagje rubber aangebracht. De nieuwe LPG-tank wordt maar liefst 80 procent lichter dan de bestaande stalen exemplaren. Behalve voor tanks kan de isotensoïde ook worden gebruikt voor heflichamen. Er is betrekkelijk weinig energie nodig om met behulp van een gas in een zak tientallen tonnen op te tillen. <

Delft University of Technology is the largest and oldest technical university in The Netherlands, founded in 1842, with over 5000 employees and about 13.500 students and 13 departments, including the Faculty of Aerospace Engineering. Its origin lies in 1940, when the Department of Aeronautics was set up in Delft as a national academic institute to promote education and research in aircraft design and development in the Netherlands. The present-day Faculty still maintains close contacts with the national end international aerospace industry.

A significant innovation in the aircraft industry was the move into space technology which resulted in the expansion of activities of the faculty to cover education and research in this new field. Consequently its name was changed to the Faculty of Aerospace Engineering.

Research in the faculty is mainly concentrated in five areas: aerodynamics, aircraft design end performance, stability end control, orbital mechanics and structures and materials.

The Structures and Materials Laboratory specializes in the development of advanced light-weight structures, conceptual and structural design and manufacturing techniques. It is not only pioneering in the field of aircraft structures and materials, but also aims to develop spin-offs for other applications.

The research efforts of the Laboratory have three major corner stones:

* Fundamental scientific research.

Successful application of new materials and design strategies can only be achieved if they are based on a thorough scientific understanding of the mechanical, physical and chemical aspects of materials and the optimal layout of structures.

* Integration of various disciplines.

The laboratory has the knowledge, skills and equipment to cover the complete development of a structure: from materials science, structural design and manufacturing techniques to the fabrication and testing of full-scale components.

* Close co-operation with the industry.

The laboratory has a strong application oriented approach. Input and questions from the industry are essential to guide the research, which is directed at gathering of engineering knowledge for the solution of practical problems. Apart from the aerospace industry, a major field of application is the transportation sector, where light-weight, performance, durability and life cycle assessment are ever returning issues. <

About the faculty